D0211371

I AM CANADA

BLOOD AND IRON

Building the Railway

by Paul Yee

Scholastic Canada Ltd.
Toronto New York London Auckland Sydney
Mexico City New Delhi Hong Kong Buenos Aires

While the events described and some of the characters in this book may be based on actual historical events and real people, Lee Heen-gwong is a fictional character created by the author, and his journal is a work of fiction.

Library and Archives Canada Cataloguing in Publication

Yee, Paul
Blood and iron : building the railway / Paul Yee.

(I am Canada)
ISBN 978-0-545-98593-2

1. Chinese--Canada--History--Juvenile literature.
2. Canadian Pacific Railway Company--History--Juvenile fiction. I. Title.
II. Series: I am Canada.

PS8597.E3B56 2010 jC813'.54 C2010-901708-0

6 5 4 3 2 1 Printed in Canada 114 10 11 12 13 14

The display type was set in Beton.
The text was set in Minion.

Dedicated to Wong Hau-hon, from Sun-wui county, Guangdong province, member of Gang 161 on the Canadian Pacific Railway in 1882.

[Translator's Note]

Lee Heen-gwong (李顯光) wrote his journal in Chinese and used dates from China's lunar calendar. This translation uses the matching dates from the Western calendar.

Heen-gwong's family came from south China, where Cantonese is the language of the region's two main ports: Hong Kong and Guang Zhou. For that reason, we give a southern look and sound to some names in English. In China today, Heen's name would be pronounced in Mandarin and written as Li Xian-guang.

In his journal, Heen-gwong did not name the places he visited. But history gives us an idea of where he landed and worked; those place names are supplied in the text.

Some place names in south China are rendered as Heen would have heard them. Other names are rendered in China's national language system pinyin.

Bound for British Columbia, 1882

March 13, 1882, Guangdong province, China

Why am I writing about being stupid? To prove I am not.

I fell, face first into river mud, and Ba cursed me. Sailors laughed until they were bent over, noses to their knees. I say they were bowing to me. Servant girls giggled, so I waved to them. Me, I was going to Gold Mountain!

I boarded the ferry, looking and smelling like an outhouse. Chickens lashed inside coops flapped and squawked on the slippery steps while pens of pigs were grunting. My father called out, "Teacher Chen is coming to say goodbye."

What for? I am his worst student and he will hate the noise here.

Teacher Chen tottered aboard and handed me a small wooden box. Its tight lid forced me to use a thumbnail to loosen it. Inside were notebooks, pencils and a penknife. Not sweet cakes. Without thinking, I blurted, "But my handwriting is bad! I know too few words!"

Ba slapped my head and barked, "Rock Brain, say thank you!"

I shoved the box back at my teacher, who refused it.

"Heen-gwong, you want people to stop calling you Rock Brain?" demanded Teacher Chen. "Then fill these books with words. Record happy times and sad, small matters and large. Sketch plans for the iron road. Come back and build one for China. And show everyone how your writing improved."

Me? When I come home, I want to put my feet up for a long rest.

Teacher Chen recited a proverb: *Know to write, rise high. Know to farm, fall low.*

I mentioned that Grandfather could write, but he gambled and lost our store!

Teacher Chen shushed me and told me to respect my elders.

"Teacher Chen, you waste money and your breath," interrupted Ba. "This son is the stupid one. That's why we call him Rock Brain!"

As the ferry headed downriver, I fretted over those words. I should have studied the busy towns and sun-black fishermen, the green paddy-fields and flocks of noisy geese. They needed to settle in my mind, in case I died in Canada.

Recently, people have stopped calling me Rock Brain, much to my delight. It has taken me all of my fourteen years to get rid of that name. Here I am, nearly as tall as Ba, and it only takes him returning from Canada and shouting out that plague of a name just once to have the entire world joining him. Am I really a Rock Brain?

If I am, would Teacher Chen give me this gift?

If I am, would Ba take me to Gold Mountain?

If I am, could I have filled this page with all these words?

Congratulations! I am a genius!

March 14

No-one talks to Ba unless he speaks first. But if I work like an adult, then Ba should treat me like one. I will be doing the same job and earning equal wages, all for the family, all to help Grandfather regain his store.

I summoned my courage and approached Ba. He sat at the front of the ferry, watching the countryside drift by, tilting his face into the morning sun.

"When do we reach Hong Kong?" I asked.

Time passed before he grunted, "Soon."

His answer, short as it was, encouraged me. "What work will I do in Gold Mountain?" I asked.

After a long pause, he muttered, "You'll see."

He walked off. I grinned. This was progress! Ba had not silenced me! I had spoken the words "Gold Mountain" aloud! I will prove that Canada can be safe for our family. Grandfather should have no more fear. It is tragic that his younger brother vanished there, but that was long ago.

At Ik-Hoi, Poy Uncle came aboard, and he squatted with Ba all morning. Later, he said to me, "Had I known you were coming, I would have brought Ah-Wing!"

His son Ah-Wing is a weakling. Me, I carried sacks of rice onto boats and off, into our store and out. I work hard as an ox, and so people think I am stupid as one.

"Your ba is wise to bring you," Poy Uncle added. "You're lucky!"

I almost shouted, Are you mad? I turned away angrily. Ba does not want me here! Ma begged him to take me along, in order to help reduce the family debt and earn more Gold Mountain money to rescue Grandfather's store.

Sudden winds picked up, the sail above our heads stiffened, and the boat doubled its speed. I lifted my arms and let the wind ripple through my sleeves and pants.

"Sit, Rock Brain!" shouted Ba. "What do you think you are? A scarecrow?"

An eagle soars through the clouds on a mission of life or death. Ba thinks I am useless, but I will be a big help to this family!

"Poy Uncle," I asked, "what work will I do on the iron road?"

"Go ask your father."

It would be easier to talk to a fish.

Today's word count is good. It was no accident that I filled a page yesterday! I *am* a genius!

March 15

Bored to death. The river is the same, all the way down. Mud and water. Water and mud. No wind. The boat limps along. Not even a genius can build words around deadly dullness. I let out my fish line into the water, but Ba told me to pull it in. I thought to accidentally drop the writing box into the river. Then I figured I could sell it later. It will be the start of my own savings!

March 19

Yesterday we boarded the big ship and left Hong Kong. When we hit deep water, our gloomy hold swayed like a signboard swinging in a typhoon. I vomited, my legs melted, and I could not walk. I was disgusted: I was no stronger than a three-year-old.

I needed to get better quickly, so I sat up, lit a candle and tried to write.

A man with a lantern is selling ginger to the seasick. Ten cash for a tiny sliver! I laugh aloud as fools summon him. Then I kick myself. If I had brought along ginger, then I would be the rich one.

March 20

The stink of vomit hangs like a soggy blanket. Some men reach the bucket just in time to throw up. Others leave a soupy mess on the floor. Our deck is dark but people smell the sour before they step or slip into it. Words and voices are muffled, so people must be covering their noses. Crossing the ocean takes forty days. Can I live that long in this stinking hold?

March 21

Ba is lucky: he is not seasick. He wolfs down food. People glare at him with death in their eyes. He brought me water yesterday but not today. Good. I do not want him thinking I am still sick.

Ma's blankets eat up my narrow bed and fall to the floor. I jump from the upper bunk and grab them before they get dirty. The floor is warm. I hear that the ship burns coal whenever the winds fail. Will such a fire burn a hole in the ship and sink us all?

Around me, men mutter about bad luck. Landlords seized their farms. High taxes ruined them. They surrendered in a clan war. They complain the food here is too measly, too plain and too soft. I wish they would clap their mouths shut. Just hearing talk of food makes me want to vomit. The men remind me of beggars at our store, waiting for tea and telling stories in return.

This joke made me laugh:

> A farmer sends two sons to buy an ox. He warns them traders will cheat them.
>
> "Sons, whatever you do," the farmer says, "don't pay what they ask."
>
> At the market, his two sons look around and find an ox. Its seller wants 3000 cash.
>
> "Don't cheat me!" says one son. "Here's 2000 cash. That's all you'll get."
>
> "Don't cheat me either," echoes his brother loudly. "Here's *my* 2000 cash!"

March 22

I went exploring, groping my way along bunkbeds. My hands landed on foreheads, feet and stomachs, so people cursed me, even kicked me. I got lost. Good thing I was counting while I stumbled along. There must be over five hundred beds.

At the eating areas, lamps are lit to let us see our food. The mush is awful, as if what we threw up has come back for a second life. Scrawny men and beggars shovel food into their mouths. I thought the Company hired only the most capable workers. Sell-Ginger cursed the iron road. He said Red

Beard Ghosts paid the Chinese workers only one-half of what they paid their own kind. The Red Beards worked the Chinese day and night until they fell down. Sell-Ginger predicted we would die from cold, illness and accidents.

"Is there no medicine in Gold Mountain to save us?" asked someone.

"Your wages are too low to afford it," snorted Sell-Ginger.

I recalled Meng-ping's father's shouting, "Don't call it Gold Mountain! Don't go there: the gold is finished. The Red Beards treat Chinese as beasts, not humans."

But the iron road pays a dollar a day. A day's wages buys 25 kilos of rice! We will earn more money than Sell-Ginger! The work cannot be all bad; this is Ba's second year in Gold Mountain. All he has said to me is: "No running on the ship. Act like an adult. No pesky questions. Men have no time for children."

If Ba spoke to me like an adult, then I would become one. Too bad he refuses.

March 24

Disaster! I saw Ba and Poy Uncle in a noisy crowd under the yellow glow of lanterns. When I went closer, I could see both men slapping coins down on a fan-tan cloth. I left before Ba could see me.

He is not to gamble! He promised Grandfather! Grandfather had hurled his own dice into the river after *his* foolish losses. Too bad it was too late. Every day the street brats surrounded me and chanted:

Run, run, run away, the cashless can't repay.

Run, run, run away, go suck a bone today.

How can Ba be playing, after all our troubles? When Ba came home, he roared at Grandfather for losing our store. I was surprised that Grandfather did not shout back. Instead, he stared at the ground and meekly said, "I did wrong. I will never play again. You must promise to do the same."

Grandfather admitting he was wrong to Ba? Unheard of!

"You play badly!" Ba fumed. "I know how to gamble. I never lose like you."

But Grandfather hounded Ba day and night until he gave in and vowed to stop.

I want to grab the money from the fan-tan cloth and run to a dark corner. Better yet, I should hurl it overboard into the ocean so that no-one gambles any more. If a boat is sailing in the opposite direction, I would hail it and swim over to board it!

Ba knows nothing about the months we waited for his money to arrive from Gold Mountain. We gnawed meat from garbage bones. Friends stopped calling, afraid we might beg for food. With no rice on hand, Ma thought the only way to feed Grandfather was to sell Little Brother, but somehow she managed to keep the family together without resorting to that. Grandfather sat in a dark corner, slapping his face and muttering, "Heaven, kick me to death. I'm truly stupid. Heaven, kick me to death."

How can I tell Ba to quit gambling? It is easy to ask about the iron road, but even Ma does not give him orders. No one tells Grandfather what to do either. When will it be my turn, when nobody can order me around?

March 25

More ruin and loss.

Once the ship reaches Canada, this Rock Brain will bolt for home. He once imagined himself as a mighty warrior who single-handedly rescues his entire family. What a fool!

This morning, I saw that Ba's bed had not been slept in. At breakfast, Poy Uncle laughed with friends, chortling so hard that rice flew from his lips. Then his face turned serious, and he told me to go tell Ba to stop gambling.

"You play beside him," I retorted. "*You* talk to him. You're his best friend!"

Last night Ba lost all his money, Poy Uncle said. The only way Ba could borrow money was to sign over his wages. Worse, Ba gambled away that loan too. Then he borrowed more money by signing over *my* wages. He lost that too. Now the only way we will have wages to take home is if Ba gambles more and wins enough to repay his loans.

My body went cold. If I could climb to the little porthole, I would throw myself off this ship. My muscles would be more useful as food for fish than as railway labour. What's the point of going to Canada if my wages don't go home to where they are needed? Grandfather will not regain the store. Ma will run out of household money. She will think of selling Little Brother again. Does Ba ever ponder her heartbreak?

I crawl back into bed. Unable to sleep, I pick up my pencil.

A man keeps crying in his bed. He is shrill and loud. His face must be wet from his sniffling. Did he get scared listening to Sell-Ginger? People shout at him to be quiet. They fear his weeping will bring bad luck. Hah! They don't know bad luck unless they know our family story!

Later

Ba took all my money even though I said I had none.

"Are you a woman?" he demanded. "A clucking hen like your Ma?" He made chicken sounds: "*Bok bok bok bok bok*. Listen, all men gamble. Look around. It's what men do. You'll do the same if you ever grow up."

His new friend Ox Uncle waited with a lantern. I wanted to run off but that would have caused Ba to lose face. Finally I reached for the eighteen coins that Ma had given to me secretly. She had warned me to hide them from Ba's eyes and safeguard them for emergencies. She had sighed wistfully and said, "I wish there was no need to say this, but you must keep money away from your father." Never before had she spoken this way to me. Those were her last words to me. How did Ba know about the coins? They had been tied inside my pants.

"Hurry, you dirty beggar," said Ox Uncle. "No one else wants your sweaty stinky coins."

The two men laughed and strolled away, leaving me in the dark.

March 27

Ba gave me back my eighteen coins, and jingled another handful of them.

"Surprised?" he sneered. "I won back every coin I lost, and took even more. Watch me and learn! A man with money, he must make it grow. He has to take it out and put it to use. If he sits on it, he may as well drop it into the outhouse."

I hated that kind of talk. Instead, I asked quietly about my railway earnings.

He sucked in an angry breath. A coin hit my face and fell to the floor. Ba snapped that there was plenty of time for him to win more money. That on his last trip, he had bet against his wages and won them back before landing. I had not known that.

"You better win," I retorted. "Otherwise I will run off and find work elsewhere."

Ba sneered that I wouldn't dare because the Company would hunt me down. I told him to wait and watch! He stomped off as I groped for the coin on my hands and knees.

March 30

Cannot write. Several days of storms. Even the gambling stopped. The sailors stopped emptying the toilet buckets, so foul smells are spreading through the deck.

April 1

Fierce waves cause the ship's walls to creak and squeal. Men are sick again. Others weep from fear but not me. Others call out to the gods.

If our ship sinks, will my journal float to Hong Kong and reach Grandfather?

April 3

I have work! I can earn money!

A young man asked me to write a letter.

"I can pay you," Wong said. "Four cash."

He must have seen me writing. But he cannot send the letter until the ship lands! Why pay now? What if he wants to write more during the trip?

I worried about knowing too few words. Then I picked up my pencil.

We started with greetings and good wishes for the New Year. His father had worked on the iron road, but went home injured and refused to let Wong go to Canada. But Wong wanted a better doctor for his father. So he secretly signed up for railway work. Now Wong apologized to his father for sneaking away just before the New Year. He said his father was right about the harsh voyage; sickness had sapped his strength. I was glad he apologized but of course I kept quiet. In our family, the only acceptable excuse for missing the New Year is if you are an ocean away, in North America. When all our relatives gather, it is the noisiest and happiest of times. And to miss all the special foods is plain stupid.

When I gave him the page from my notebook, he yelled, "I won't pay 4 cash! You used a pencil!"

He argued that someone could erase my words and change his meaning. He wanted a letter in ink. I told him no one can make changes and get away with it. It is absolutely impossible. Besides, who can do brushwork while riding these waves? We argued until I settled on 2 cash. He walked away grinning. I really am Rock Brain!

April 4

I strolled around and banged on my writing box with a stick, shouting I would write letters, 4 cash per page.

Ba slapped my head, hard. "What do you think we are?" he shouted. "Beggars? Anyone who hires this boy will have to deal with me!"

When no customers came forward, I wanted to tell the crowd how Ba had pledged away my wages. But I did no such thing. Our family name is one of the best.

Now I can go back to sleeping. I nap all day and all night. Why not? In the dark here, no one can tell time. I am forever tired, no matter how much I sleep.

April 6

At mealtime, a man hurled his soggy rice and dried fish at the Red Beard sailor. He shouted that we deserved better food. Men yelled support, banging on their bunks and stomping their feet. The Company man came down and called for quiet. Passengers lobbed food and foul names at him. We laughed when he clambered up the ladder as fast as he could go.

At first, we ate beans, cabbage and melons in the soupy rice along with pork. It tasted so bad that people said the cooks were not Chinese. Then the kitchen used up the pigs and greens. We got dried vegetables and dried shrimp, tidbits lost in the soggy rice. The cooks soaked them in salt water. Everyone got thirsty. There was never enough drinking water.

April 8

Today, I asked Wong why he had written the letter so early.

He felt guilty for leaving his family, especially at New Year. He could not sleep, so he wanted to get his worries out of his head and onto paper. He said, "Can I ask you a question?"

Not another letter, I thought, not for 2 cash.

He said, "Was I right to disobey my father and go to work on the iron road?"

Luckily, I had just filled my mouth with rice, so I chewed slowly. The best way to make a father happy? Do exactly what he says. Or do what you think is best. Who knows? I glanced at Wong, and saw how sad he looked. So I told him a story instead:

> A little boy wants to work in the family store. The father says he is too weak. The boy runs to the warehouse and grabs a small rice sack in each hand. He thrusts his arms out and stands in the shape of a cross all afternoon. Next day, he takes a larger rice sack in each hand and stands the same way. The following day, he does the same thing with two even larger rice sacks. He calls his father to come see his strength.
>
> "My, my," says his father. "Now, how about putting some rice into those sacks?"

April 11

I lit my candle and opened my journal. Ba said, "Pencils cost money. Don't write useless things."

I got angry and forgot what to record. Ba has no idea what I put down here. Today I think about the men on this ship.

Song-Flower wanders about singing Cantonese opera. He does both men's and women's voices.

People shout to him to sing such-and-such a tune, but he never responds.

One man steals light from the gamblers to read. They insult him.

"Scholar, you'll go blind squinting at words!"

"Scholar, aren't you afraid to dirty your hands in Gold Mountain?"

"Books are useless, Scholar. Better tie them around your legs to keep warm."

Every now and then, Scholar settles into horse position and stands braced for hours, getting strong for the work ahead.

Stir-the-Pot keeps shouting at the sailors about the terrible food.

Two brothers go everywhere together. When one uses the toilet, the other waits outside for him. When one gambles, the other stands behind to guard him. They sleep on the floor, not in bunk beds. They rarely speak, so no one knows their surname.

Men gather around Miner. He lives alone in the wilderness of Gold Mountain and follows the smell of gold wherever it takes him. He says the rivers are cold but full of fast-moving fish. When rumours of new gold are heard, a lonely mountainside suddenly teems like an anthill with gold-seekers. Each day tests his brains and muscles. He has no fear of Red Beard Ghosts. He said we should take care when we are near them, but otherwise there is no need to be scared. I feel better hearing that.

Someone asks if it is true that men die of cold in Gold Mountain. He nods.

Maybe I should follow Miner. But Meng-ping's father said the gold is all gone.

April 13

Ba asked me for money. I handed him the coin he had tossed onto the floor.

"More," he said.

He took my eighteen coins without saying a word.

I hate it when he treats me like a servant.

April 14

Last night Ba did not come back. I pray he is having a run of good luck.

April 15

Again, Ba did not use his bed. It is two nights in a row. I cannot sleep. Ba claims to be clever enough to win at any game. If only I could believe him! He has always worked far from home. No-one in town ever built a new house from gambling success. Old Choi down the lane won a fortune and bragged about moving to the capital, but then he lost everything in another game. Ma bought a set of new dishes from Old Choi's wife when she was selling her goods in order to pay rent.

The problem isn't about winning; it's about *keeping* the winnings. If Ba let me guard his winnings, then we could easily regain our wages.

April 16

Someone died today. How could that happen?

We were all inspected in Hong Kong before we boarded this ship. A Red Beard doctor peered into our eyes, checked our tongues and listened to our pulse. He dismissed a few men, who left unhappily. We took off our clothes and Company men shot snakes of forceful water at us.

The Company man searched the dead man's belongings, looking for a name. He found nothing and called out, "Did anyone talk to him?"

No-one replied.

"Speak up!" shouted the Company man. "He must have talked to someone!"

Finally Sell-Ginger said, "His surname was Ong. He's from Chek-Hom."

The Company man needed help to roll the body into a blanket. No one moved. That was when I felt the cold in my hands. Back home, we saw bodies in the river and dead beggars on the street. We poked at them with sticks. Corpses never bothered me. Until now.

April 17

Pranksters whistled and made ghostly noises last night, trying to frighten people. Others shouted at them to be quiet and show respect for the dead.

Old Ong's bottom bunk was empty, but people were too scared to take it. Ba asked if I wanted it, but I shook my head.

Poy Uncle muttered that Old Ong should have died earlier, before we got so close to Gold Mountain. Now Old Ong's ghost would follow us ashore.

No one knows the cause of death. Some people blame the Company: not enough fresh air and clean water. Others say if that was true, then more men would have died. They say Ong was sick and had no idea how to care for himself.

April 18

Fights broke out. Scholar was standing quietly in horse position when someone flung a bowl of water into his face.

"This horse looks thirsty!" said the man. "This horse stinks!"

Scholar's hand and foot lashed out and the man landed on the floor. He leapt up and charged, yelling like a crazy man. Scholar blocked his arm, and punched his stomach. The man fell down, clutching himself. When he crept away, Scholar was back in horse position.

Then two men fought in the lineup for the toilet. One man accused another of stepping ahead of him, while the latter claimed the first man had gone away to talk to a friend. These men knew nothing about fighting; other passengers easily pulled them apart.

April 19

On the third day after, people light incense and candles at Old Ong's bed.

People say no-one knew Old Ong was sick. He never complained. They thought if he chewed ginger and slept, then he would get better, like everyone else.

Ba took me to pay respects. Just as we arrived, Sell-Ginger banged the wooden bed and shouted, "Return to China, all of you! You're too sickly to build an iron road. Look, one of you just died. How will you worms survive? Do you want to die?"

"We signed contracts," someone shouted. "We ate the ship's food. We owe money. We have to work!"

"Your lives are more important," Sell-Ginger pleaded. "Run and hide when the ship pulls into the docks."

If he is so scared, someone says, then he should stay home.

"We built the Great Wall," Ba said quietly. "Of course we can do this job."

"I came to warn you," Sell-Ginger explained. "My son died on the iron road. Please, spare your loved ones this grief."

"All of us, we have lost family to Gold Mountain," replied Ba. "We know the risks. Leave us alone."

After Sell-Ginger left, men crowded around Ba to praise him. My friend Wong was among them. He raised his thumb at me. I have never heard Ba speak so well.

April 21

I changed my mind and will not return to China right away, panting like a drowning rat. Little Brother will look down at me. The townspeople will point to me and call me a coward. They will say I feared hard work, feared the Red Beards. They will treat me like a corpse.

I tell myself this: helping to repay Ba's debts is the same as helping Grandfather regain his store.

If Ba wins back our wages, I want my account to hold a respectable amount of earnings.

April 23

Poy Uncle announces that land is nearing. Each day feels a little cooler than before. Some passengers have started packing. They annoy the lazy ones, who call out, "What's the rush? Can't wait to become a slave?"

Poy Uncle said that this is the most dangerous part of a voyage. Sailors cannot see the rocks below the water, especially at night.

I think no place is safe, except for home.

April 24

Last night, our blankets were missing. Ba would not answer me when I asked where they were. I knew right away he had sold them to get gambling money. Now we will freeze to death in Gold Mountain.

April 25

Yesterday Ba sold his padded jacket. Good thing the voyage is almost over. Otherwise, Ba might sell his pants and really make a fool of himself.

April 26

Ba asked if I was going home.

I said no.

He almost smiled. "Glad to hear that," he said. "Otherwise, I would have beaten you until you were lame. And Grandfather would have thanked me."

I made the right decision. I'm a genius!

April 27, Victoria, British Columbia

I give up. The whole world can call me Rock Brain now.

When the ship docked, men surged to the ladders, desperate for daylight and fresh air. We shouted and banged on the hatches. No sailors came. We heard footsteps above, and heavy things were dragged over the ceiling. No doubt we would be last to leave.

One hatch creaked open. Men rushed from the other ladders and pressed in so urgently that I thought someone would get trampled to death. The Company man, a fellow named Leung, brought helpers and shouted at us to form groups of thirty.

"Find people of the same surname, or from your village area," he advised. "That way you won't fight so much."

We rushed to get our luggage. I followed Ba into a group, mostly his gambling friends. Then we waited. And waited. I climbed up a bunk for a look. The gangs were trickling by two tables at the foot of the ladder. A clerk recorded each man's name and home village. Those who had schooling insisted on the correct words. But the clerks refused to make corrections.

We were crushed together, twisting toward the tables, fighting to breathe. We cursed the Company. Every now and then, a name sailed back from the front. Someone at the rear cried out and started pushing forward. We were packed so tightly that skinny men dropped to their hands and knees, and crawled through people's legs, dragging their bundles behind them. The Company man shouted "Move back!" but no one did.

Then I recalled one pencil was still at my bunk, tucked between the boards for nighttime writing. I pushed through the crowd toward the beds. It was like a beggar trying to reach a rich man's door. I wanted to jump up and sprint over people's heads. After finding my pencil, I faced a solid wall of men's backs. Then I heard my name being called.

"That's me!" I shouted. "Let me through!"

With a running start, I threw myself into the crowd. People shoved back, cursing. Every step was a battle. "They're calling me!" I screamed, "My people are leaving! Let me pass!"

At every step, I groped for my backpack. I wormed through the throng, inch by painful inch. I saw the ladder and the open hatch get closer. Then a flash of news crackled through the crowd. The people melted away and I quickly slid forward. But the hatch was closed and our hold was black again.

"Where are the Company people?" I shouted.

"Boat's full," grunted a voice in the shadows, "so we go tomorrow."

I flew up and banged at the hatch. "I need to get off! I got left behind!"

No one heard me. I dropped to the floor, shaken. Ba will be furious, I thought. And what if Ba thinks I stayed behind on purpose?

He will disown me.

April 28, New Westminster, British Columbia

What a big scare this afternoon! My body went so cold I thought I was dying.

I carried my baggage ashore and followed some men to a boat. Then more men came off our ship. But they headed to another pier, to another berth. Two boats?

I sprinted back to the ship and shouted at the Company man, "Yesterday's boat, where did it go?"

"Yale."

"Are today's boats going there?" I demanded.

"Only one."

"Which one?"

"The paddlewheeler."

I calmed down, feeling like a stupid chicken. I was glad to see Wong Brother on my boat. He told me not to worry about Ba; the Chinese company is well organized and it would be easy to find him.

We sailed through rocky islands and sometimes swung so close to land that men at the railing shouted in alarm. Did the captain understand Chinese? But he reversed the paddlewheel just in time and avoided the deadly rocks.

The cold winds made me shiver. The islands were nothing but cliffs and forests. Big slug-like animals lay on the rocky beach of one island. Their tiny heads had no ears, their fat round bodies had no legs, and their arms were short flaps. They weren't fish, but they weren't land animals either. How strange!

At the mouth of the river, its muddy current poured into the clear ocean. The shores were thick with trees, but many paths led to the water and to long boats carved from big trees. The local people had built big houses from planks of wood. Tall poles carved with animal shapes stood near those homes.

Then the water took on a different life. The river spurted by, sweeping entire trees along, bouncing them to and fro like twigs. The captain steered with care so that the trees did not swing in and plug the paddlewheel. We fought the strong current while bitter black smoke billowed from the steamer's smokestack. What fishes could survive such wild waters?

When we stopped, I asked to go ashore to look for Ba. The new Company man said yesterday's boat had not left anyone behind. Besides, this was not Yale. He blew smoke from his cigar into my face, as if I were a servant.

The town sits on a hill with many buildings. Some roofs rise to a steep point; others are flat. A road runs to the top of the hill, to a very large building. Is it a temple?

A Company guard stopped us from going ashore. Instead, hot food was brought aboard: great pots of rice and smaller pots of meat and pickled greens. I filled my bowl four times! Finally, a meal with properly cooked rice!

Wong Brother sent over two men who asked me to write letters. They want their families to know we have arrived safely. Ba should be writing to Ma and Grandfather.

I write until the boss of the gamblers curses me

for stealing light from his lantern. More men want to join the game, and I block the way.

April 29, Fort Hope, British Columbia

I have given up chasing Ba. I am cold with fear at being lost, alone and left behind. Am I a bad son?

I would be stupid to chase a man who cannot be caught now. The Company knows where every worker is. Otherwise, how would letters from China get forwarded to the right people? With so many new workers arriving all at once, the Company man says it is impossible to track down one man right away – it takes time.

I am facing the tallest, biggest mountains that I have ever seen. Their sides are straight and smooth as walls. The hills at home are mere bumps by comparison. How can we build an iron road over such a barrier?

A small boat will take me to a work site. The travel is finished; the idleness must end. Now I must work and prove myself. I must not give in to fear.

Last night, people rushed for sleeping spots inside the steamer. Not everyone found room. I slept outside, on the deck, shivering with a shirt wrapped around my head. Wong Brother asked why I had no blanket. I did not say. Later, he shared his blanket with me.

The Company sent tea and bread. The tea was already cool.

Two crews left the boat, to work near this town. Then the Company man learned two men had sneaked off the boat. Right away, he fired the guard.

An elderly man boarded the steamer. He had dark skin, golden brown in colour. His face looked somewhat Chinese, and his hair hung black and straight. He wore Western clothes. The sailors pointed to the stairs and gestured for him to go down to our deck. The man shook his head. The sailors shouted at him. The man paid them no attention. Then they picked him up and slung him down to us like a sack of rice. The man was not happy and shouted angrily at the sailors in a language I did not understand.

A Chinese man had come aboard by himself. "Is that man Chinese?" I asked, pointing at the older man.

No. I was told that the Red Beards called that man *Yeen-Cheen*. His people lived throughout Canada, and had been here long before the Red Beards. The land along this part of the river belonged to a band called Sto:lo.

When I told the Chinese man I wanted to go to Yale, he said Yale stood on the land of the Tait people. That old man looked like a Tait man, he added. And the boat would stop first at Fort Hope, also on Tait territory. Farther north was the land of the Nlaka'pamux people, site of the dangerous rock work being done for the railway. The Chinese man spoke loudly, proud that he knew so much. I quickly wrote down the sounds of the names and the locations of their lands. Not only did that local man look a bit Chinese, but he also reminded me of how we say, I am a Toi-San person, or I am a Jung-San person.

As we went upriver, the mountains moved in. Silently, they grew larger and larger. The green and black on them brightened and then fell dull as clouds moved in and out. When I looked behind, the mountains had closed like a giant door.

Along the river, gold miners shovelled river dirt into boxes. The Chinese waved at us when we called out. Sto:lo people fished with spears and nets. I wanted to yell for the boat to slow down. Then I worried that Ba had failed to reach Yale.

Fort Hope had a few buildings and several steamboats at its shore. The mountain behind loomed as a forbidding obstacle. When I saw Wong Brother trudge down the gangplank with his crew, I panicked and ran to the Company man and told my story again.

He announced that the men who reached Yale yesterday had already been sent to work sites. "Better join a crew here," he grunted. "You're wasting Company time."

I stood on land but felt as if I were clinging to a one-board raft in the churning river. I saw gangs of workers come off the boat and get prodded onto another one. They shouted for friends to hurry. Company men screamed at porters who were loading and unloading crates and vats. I dodged wheelbarrows and men staggering under heavy bales. They cursed me to move aside. One steamer kept tooting its whistle. No-one stood alone, and that scared me.

I swallowed my alarm and ran to Wong Brother. There was no one else to turn to. But he was with the gambler who had kicked me away from his lantern. "Who's this?" he demanded.

When I gave my name, the gambler declared that all Wongs despised all Lees. He told me to go join another group.

"*Your* village battled the Lees," Wong Brother retorted. "*My* village had no trouble with them."

Good thing the Company man had followed me, dragging along a fellow Chinese dressed in Western clothing. This was the man who would keep the book on my hours and wages, I was told.

But these two were sworn enemies. The Company man ordered Bookman to add me to his roster. Bookman spat to one side and said he didn't have his book with him. He looked sullen. I think the Company man pulled him out of a game with friends. The two men argued about who should be giving out orders, and finally Bookman stomped away.

For once, I wished Ba was near. He may not think much of me, but he always stands up for our family name.

May 4, Fraser Valley, west of Fort Hope

My hands cannot hold a pen. Too bad I lacked this excuse when I suffered Teacher Chen's classroom tyranny. If he sees this, he will exclaim, "What is Rock Head doing? Writing with his left hand?"

At every joint of my fingers, blisters puff out. When I try to make a fist, my hand becomes a claw.

But I must write. It is all I can do to stop my fears, for I regret coming here. Animals howl through the night as I await huge jaws and fangs. When it rains, our tents leak. The nights are cold and my new blanket is thin. Gold Mountain crushes me, for I am too tired to sleep and then too tired to work.

Each day we tramp through the forest, axes on our shoulders. The site is far and there is no trail. Path markers, chopped into trees, guide us over rocks and fallen trees and through swamps and tangled underbrush. We never know where our feet will land, on living things or dead. My feet are safe in the leather boots that Bookman urged me to buy, but now I owe the Company more money than ever before.

Our job is to open a wide path through dense forest. It is madness. The trees are so tall that their tops cannot be seen. Their branches are heavy with needles; overhead they reach out and interlock like fingers. They stand straight as pillars at a temple but press close together, smothering us in darkness that lingers all day. The trees grow so big that six or seven men with arms linked cannot circle their trunks. Bookman shouts at us, "Your trees must fall AWAY from the iron road!"

We all raced to be first to chop down a giant. At first we laughed like children. Then we realized these trees had stood for hundreds of years. Pock Face and Mouse succeeded late in the day. Their tree crashed and filled the sky with crackling and hissing. Other trees sheared limbs and branches off the falling tower. Birds flew up to scold us. Buck Tooth and Little Uncle were next, but their tree failed to hit the ground. It struck its neighbour and both trees stayed standing, one against the other, like old friends.

At day's end, we heard yelling and a loud crash. Buck Tooth and Little Uncle cut another tree and aimed it against the first one. When the second tree fell, it toppled the first one.

For now, we are camped by the river. When we clear away enough trees at the site, the camp will be moved there in order to save us time and strength.

We are seven men in a tent. The other tents have six, except for the cooking tent where Bookman, Cook and Helper sleep.

No-one wanted an extra person in their tent.

"Not enough room here," Gambler snarled. "Go to the cooking tent."

There, Bookman kicked me out.

Finally Wong Brother pulled me in. But his friends want me to change tents each night so that the entire crew shares the overcrowding.

May 5

Nights belong to the animals, who bark like dogs but shriller. There is no escaping them. One animal opens its mouth, a second one answers, and then twenty are yelping and howling. Finally they stop. Then, just as I fall asleep, one animal growls and the howling starts all over. How can anyone work without a good rest?

My arms and shoulders are sore. My back and feet ache. My eyes itch from the sweat. To lie down, turn over or get up is painful, and sleeping on rocks worsens the pain.

May 6

When one man's axe got stuck in a tree, he pulled and yanked at it, cursing all the while. Then he braced one foot against the tree and heaved. The axe-head popped out, the man fell back, and the iron slammed into his forehead. His partner screamed, thinking he was dead. But by the time Bookman arrived, the man was sitting up. His new name is Big Lump, like the one on his head.

May 7

After six days, we get rest. Bookman should have told us earlier, to let us look forward to this. But he has no heart and does not want people to smile.

Men washed their clothes in the river and laid them out to dry. They heated water and washed themselves. Me? I slept in the tent all morning, even though the sun was out. I dreamed of home and bowls of soft white rice, fragrant and steaming.

Watermelon asked me to write a letter. Bookman charges 7 cash, so of course I can offer a better price.

On the first day, Toothpick went into the woods to squat. He got lost and no one heard him calling. At midday, someone finally noticed. Bookman sent us off in pairs to look for him. "Make sure you can find your way back!" he called out.

Wong Brother muttered, "How are we supposed to do that?"

When Toothpick was found, Bookman shouted, "Fool, stay closer!"

"He cannot," someone quipped. "He makes the worst stink in the world!"

"Even his mother runs away!" said a tent-mate.

Then Gambler stepped on a frog. When it leapt up, so did he, screaming like a woman and landing on the man behind him. Someone shouted out, "Pity the frog!"

Next, I must write to Ba. I will say I chased him up the river until discovering that his crew had already been dispatched. Like a good (and stupid) son, I will ask him to forgive my foolishness. The Company will eventually forward the letter to him, and then I suppose I must join his crew once he tells me where they are.

May 8

Somehow Pock Face's axe-head loosened and flew off the handle. It hurtled through the air and got lost. Axe-heads are expensive, so we hunted high and low. We finally found it deep in a tree and then told him to work on one tree at a time.

Now we cut up fallen trees and drag sections away. Today's tree was four feet round. One of us stands on top, the other stays on the ground, and together we push and pull at a long saw. Keeping balanced on the curved top is tricky; both Wong Brother and I have fallen off. We are also delayed when the saw gets stuck. We squirt oil into the crack, and pound in wedges.

When Crew Boss sauntered by and spoke, Bookman translated: "Be careful near the end. Get ready to run when the cut-off end drops."

Wong Brother snapped, "Does he think we're stupid?"

May 9

Slant Mouth Bing bragged about felling a tree six feet across. He held one hand above his head to show the trunk's height — on its side! It was 476 years old, he said, born in the Ming dynasty! He had counted the rings in the stump.

Cook exclaimed, "Can you count that high?" and everyone laughed.

May 10

My tree had 305 rings; it was from Ming times too. Slant Mouth Bing's partner Pretty Boy hurt his hand. His fingers got crushed when the men tried to free a trapped saw blade.

May 11

Wong Brother hobbles around on a makeshift crutch. We were moving the cut end of a log when it dropped onto his foot. His big toe turned black, the toenail cracked and bled, but he kept on working.

May 13

Money God was rushing back to camp when he slipped on a wet log and fell. Then he screamed and flung away the thorny vines he had grabbed. Pinpricks of blood covered his palms like stars in the night sky. Big Uncle said, "Red in your hands is good luck," and gave him the nickname Money God. He worries the thorns were poisonous.

May 14

Rest day. The men playing paper dominoes hooted and chortled in their tent. Rain kept them inside, and left our tents stinking from wet and unwashed bodies.

Then we had visitors. Two gold miners, Seto and Soo, were heading upriver. We all crowded into Big Uncle's tent as Cook brought hot tea. Everyone had questions. Was there gold to be found now? Had they met other railway workers? How far was the nearest town? Were any Red Beard Ghosts nearby? Where was the iron road? And the fire cars?

Only 7 miles of iron had been laid, said Seto. The entire road will be 400 miles long in this province.

Big Lump exclaimed, "It will take a lifetime to build!"

"By then your head will be the size of a house!" said Pretty Boy.

As for the fire cars, they said, "Go see the trains for yourself! Go to Yale!"

Soo was surprised to hear that none of our crew had run off to try gold mining. He said he could always spot newcomers: they wore new shoes.

Toothpick found it strange that workers came from so far away to build the iron road.

"Not enough people here," replied Soo. "That is precisely why they are building a railway. It will bring in tens of thousands of people from the other side of Canada."

Later, Bookman warned us that Company agents watched for deserters in all towns. He had crept to the tent and secretly listened to us! What a snake!

May 15

A falling tree hit Little Uncle and left his right arm useless. Bookman blamed him for being careless but Little Uncle denied it was his fault. The tree had been cut so that it would fall away from him, but it suddenly moved on its own.

May 17

Six Sto:lo men walked through and watched us work. I had to re-read my earlier page to get the right name. One man carried a long gun, while two others carried nets for fishing. Another had a shiny axe hanging from his belt. Between them and us, we had no words to speak to one another. Bookman greeted them, but not in Chinese, and walked them to our camp.

Later, Cook said he cooked rice for the visitors and served them strong tea.

May 18

I almost died today. Even now I want to fall on my knees and thank the heavens and the ancestors for keeping me alive. I never imagined the breath of life tasted so sweet. Wong Brother and I had felled a tree, but it failed to drop. Instead, it got caught, high up, by the sturdy branches of a neighbour. We pushed and shoved but couldn't budge our tree. All we could do was chop at the neighbour, to bring it down too. As we hacked away, the neighbour twisted suddenly and our first tree shot down like a massive boulder. Its leaves and branches flicked my arm as I tried to back away. From the ground, I thought the tree looked skinny and light, but it would have flattened my life if I had been caught under it. Wong Brother called me stupid for not moving faster. But it happened too quickly. I wanted to shout out that just as easily the tree could have fallen in *his* direction. But I would never call him stupid.

A boat brought supplies, mostly firewood. Cook cannot burn the trees we cut down because they are wet and do not burn well. Helper collects dry branches and asks us to bring back dry timber we find. Cook fears running out of firewood, and will not make hot breakfasts.

We looked longingly at the steamer, bobbing on the river. No doubt all the workers shared one thought: it would be heavenly to leave this wretched place.

May 20

I worked eighteen days so I earned $18. But for each working day, the Company deducts lodging at 9 cents, meals at 12 cents, Bookman's fee at 1 cent, and ship ticket repayment at 20 cents. My blanket and boots cost $6.50, so my total expenses came to $14.48. All I earned was $3.52.

I felt sick and had to sit down. I earned only one-fifth of what I had expected. It was hard to believe, and I checked all the numbers. I went through them three times and found no mistakes.

The few men who already owned boots had more money in their accounts. They were the most cheerful. I tried to see the bright side of things. So far, Ba's gambler friend can only get $3.52 from me, and only if Ba doesn't repay the debt beforehand.

What if Ba fails to win back my wages? Then I am someone's slave!

I want to earn real wages, cash that I can spend on whatever I want. I work hard but get treated as a child: nothing is mine and everyone orders me around. I should do as Ba does: gamble with my money and lose it and deepen our family troubles. Let's see how he feels about it then!

May 21

I feel a little better about money because I wrote letters for Big Lump and Pock Face today. Pock Face told his wife to speed up the matchmaking so that their eldest daughter can get married by the year's end. I hope he has lots of money to spend on an extravagant banquet.

May 23

Two days of rain left us cold and miserable. When Gambler got his food tonight, he yelled at Cook. "Do you eat this? For three weeks we've eaten the same trash! I feed my dog better than this!"

I have never seen such low-grade food either. Because the rice was boiled, dried and flattened in China, then re-soaked in hot water, there are many grains that stay hard. The men are always spitting them out.

Gambler was in a foul mood after getting his thumb badly squashed. He might have attacked Cook if Cook had not waved his cleaver at him.

I make sure to watch my hands carefully so nothing will slow me down at work. I don't want my fingers crushed in a tree.

May 24

Bookman told us this morning it was the Queen of Canada's birthday. We did not have to work but we decided to go earn money. Good thing all the men think alike.

May 25

A saw blade cut Pretty Boy's hand, and blood gushed out. We tied cords around his wrist, and he raised his hand high, but blood kept spurting. Later, he rolled his hand into his shirt and kept on working. When Big Uncle told him to drink beef soup to restore his blood, we all laughed. Might as well tell him to eat roast duck.

May 27

Limp Leg has been coughing ever since the rain soaked him. Cook gave him strong tea while Crew Boss fed him spoonfuls of red liquid. Nothing helped. His tent-mates complain they cannot sleep.

Limp Leg reminds me of Grandfather. They have the same sad smile. When Grandfather disciplined me at home, I hated him. Until he gave me a candy next day. He never said a word, just smiled to tell me that he hated doing Ba's job.

When Pretty Boy's hand swelled up, Big Uncle pierced it and let the pus ooze out. Then he sprinkled Iron-Hit powder on the wound. Everyone shouted out advice but Pretty Boy told us to leave him alone.

May 28

We met five workers from downriver. I remembered them from the same boat that brought us to this site.

We saw one another and burst out laughing because we looked exactly the same. Thin and tired. Filthy clothes. Dirty bandages. Cracked boots. Tangled hair sprouting from furry foreheads. Straggly beards. I had no stubble, but grime covered my chin.

They were looking for a runaway co-worker, a man who had been spooked after an accident killed his friend. But these lazy visitors were hardly searching. They carried jugs of rice wine, bought from a Chinese merchant rafting down the river. We said if they should see the wine merchant again, they should send him to us.

"Do you have any money?" they asked.

"Do you?" we asked.

We laughed again. Their bookman advanced cash to them from their wages. Our bookman is too lazy.

Later the Sto:lo men from earlier brought us a dead deer. In return, Cook gave them all the tea he had. Cook had no idea how to butcher the animal, but Gambler had worked as a butcher in China. So Pretty Boy got some hearty soup to drink.

May 30

Limp Leg slept in camp yesterday but today he came with us. His cough was not better but he did not want to miss work.

We got new pickled vegetables with our rice and dried fish. Cook said they had arrived with the firewood on the steamer a few days ago.

"Why didn't you serve it earlier?" growled Gambler. "I was going to murder you in your sleep last night!"

May 31

One minute Slant Mouth Bing was working and the next minute he was dead. I still cannot believe it.

A thick slab of tree split off and dropped on him, crushing even his timepiece. Then we saw how the tree was black and soft, rotting from the inside. Crew Boss shook his head sadly. We were all grim and quiet except for Limp Leg, who moaned and wailed.

Bookman told us to bury Slant Mouth Bing right away. Big Uncle protested, "Our contracts say our bodies will get shipped back to China."

"Otherwise his family will think he was sold into slavery," chimed in Mouse.

"Are you stupid?" retorted Bookman. "Forty to fifty days on a ship? The coffin will be full of maggots by then."

Instead, he wrote in his book about Slant Mouth Bing dying on the job. He asked three men to sign the page as proof that the truth had been told. I looked away but Wong Brother pointed to me and said, "He knows words."

I wrote my name and home village. Wong Brother saw my age and his eyes widened in surprise. Bookman wrote Slant Mouth Bing's real name: Wong Jee Jeung. His father had wanted him to be an army general.

To my surprise, Bookman took a shovel and helped with the digging.

June 3

We took rice and a whole cooked fish to Slant Mouth Bing's grave. Helper lit candles and incense sticks. When the men asked where the fish had come from, Cook pointed to me. Yesterday I took my hook and line and went to the small stream. Bookman pulled out a jug of rice wine, and poured it over the grave. It felt strange to be bowing here. It was like being back in China.

The forest hung over us like storm clouds. It made me think of Hell. An iron road is madness, I thought. It's a road to nowhere! How could Ba come back here for such miserable work?

These days, with every swing of my axe, I

glance up at the tree, to make sure nothing might drop onto me. I screamed and jumped back once, but it turned out to be just a dead branch. I felt very stupid.

June 4

Wong Brother and Big Lump followed me as I left the camp.

"Going fishing?" asked Wong Brother. He grinned and held up a hook and line. "Remember, my father was an iron road worker too," he said. "Like yours."

Wong Brother and Big Lump are distantly related, so they kept naming people they might know in common. They talked about getting a map, and marking the spot where Slant Mouth Bing was buried. They want to be able to come back here and remember him.

We brought back five fish, each of them good-sized. Cook and Helper grumble that I make more work for them, but at least the workers have fresh meat.

June 6

Today Money God and Big Lump felled the biggest tree yet. Its trunk was eight feet across. Money God counted over six hundred rings. This tree was from the Yuan dynasty! Big Lump said the Company should be building the iron road to go around such trees instead of chopping them down. That way, train passengers can have impressive things to see.

June 9

They were lifting timber when Gambler slipped. The log landed on his foot and left it swollen and red. His boot had to be cut open to free the foot. Big Uncle said the gods were punishing him for shouting at Limp Leg. Gambler retorted that every crew member had been injured at least once. I never knew so many accidents had happened. He asked for needle and thread to save his boot.

June 10

When we returned to camp, Limp Leg was gone. He was in no condition to go anywhere! Cook said the boat delivered supplies, and Limp Leg boarded it for Yale. Big Uncle did not believe this but Cook swore it was the truth. He said Limp Leg did not want to cause more trouble here.

This is terrible. If Limp Leg dies, it will be our fault. All of us will have his blood on our hands. We chased Limp Leg away because we feared his sickness. The situation worsened a few days ago when Gambler, Buck Tooth and Little Uncle moved out of Limp Leg's tent. They didn't want to get ill. Mind you, not everyone was cruel. Pock Face and Mouse stayed with Limp Leg, and neither one of them is sick.

Limp Leg rested for a day and returned to work yesterday. Big Uncle advised him to rest but he would not listen. In the middle of the morning, he collapsed, coughing blood. For the remainder of the day, he sat against a tree with his eyes closed. I gave him water. Big Uncle asked Bookman to send Limp Leg to Yale, to the Chinese doctor. Limp Leg said he had no money. Big Uncle offered to lend him some. Limp Leg refused it. Little Uncle, Gambler and Buck Tooth got angry. They demanded Bookman send Limp Leg to Yale whether he wanted to go or not. They shouted that another death in the crew would bring bad luck to all of us. Limp Leg begged them to let him earn a living. He was crying.

I should have spoken up, and called for kindness to be shown to sick people. But I am the youngest in this crew, and no-one listens to me.

June 11

I should have gone fishing, but the mosquitoes are especially thick around the mud. The rain and swamps breed large amounts of bugs, much more than at home.

Bookman handed me a letter, from Ba. I read it and dropped it into the fire. He didn't say a word about coming to fetch me, or where his camp was. Should we not be together? What kind of a father is he? We are an ocean away from home! He should be watching over me! I came to work for the sake of the family, but Ba hardly treats me like family. Well, I am fine without him!

Then I felt like a bad son and tried desperately to recall his words. Day and night, he said, he worried about me. He had tried to leave the first boat and find me. But the crowd around him was too thick. The boss of the Chinese company told him I would be safe as long as I stayed with a gang. Lastly, Ba said I must work hard and watch my expenses.

I think the real reason he does not want me with him is he knows how much I hate gambling.

June 13

This morning, Big Lump went into the woods to squat. He crawled back, blood streaming from his chest. A big dark animal had sprung up and slashed him so hard that he flew through the air. He heard a loud roar and waited for the beast to eat him. But when he looked up, the animal was gone. We would not have believed him if he had not been bleeding so badly. Everyone plans to stay closer to the camp from now on. It is going to stink terribly!

June 14

Men are still joking about today's bad accident. I cannot believe they are so hard-hearted.

Pock Face was chopping at a tough soggy tree root when his axe sliced his foot. He howled with such drama that everyone ran to him. When I arrived, the axe was still stuck in his foot, its handle poking into the air. Blood seeped through the cracked boot. Pock Face's muddy hands fumbled at the blood, as if trying to scoop it back into his foot. Two men held Pock Face as Money God yanked out the axe. Pock Face screamed like a pig being slaughtered. Then the men held his leg high as Big Uncle pressed on the cut. When the bleeding stopped and got cleaned up, the wound looked smaller than expected. The thick boot had provided good protection, but it will be many days before Pock Face can walk again.

This happened when we were clearing the ground. We had done all we can for the new camp, so Crew Boss used explosive powder to remove the tree stumps. Bookman took us deep into the woods. We heard a thud, and then another and another. Bookman listened carefully and counted, and then he led us back to the site. It looked as if a typhoon had swept through. Stumps were overturned and uprooted. Wood chips and timber pieces lay everywhere. Wet earth clung to the trees. We broke down the larger stumps and dragged them away.

Big Lump was upset too, at missing the explosions.

"Nothing to see," we told him. "No pretty colours, no fireworks."

June 15

Big Lump got up this morning to work. At breakfast, he gasped and bent over in pain. When he lifted the cloth from his wounds, his entire chest was flaming red. Greenish pus leaked from the cuts. Iron-Hit powder was no use. Big Uncle called for cold boiled water to wash him and to cool him down. We walked quietly to work. We had all assumed Big Lump would recover quickly because he was one of the strongest men in the crew.

June 17

We had a visitor: Bookman's boss, the contractor. He is a Chan, from Lian Chang Company. He came to pay respects to Slant Mouth Bing. The crew followed him to the grave, where he lit candles and burned incense and spirit money. At the clearing, he praised us for working hard. The iron road was Canada's biggest undertaking, he said, and we were lucky to be working on it. The iron road would change the face of the land. Then he hurried off to talk to Crew Boss.

Money God cursed and muttered, "Lucky? What's he talking about? People are dying!"

Big Uncle chased Chan and mentioned Big Lump's injuries. Chan promised to see him but when we got back to camp, Big Lump said no-one had visited him.

June 18

Bad news from far away smothered us like the black fog of bugs in which we live. We brooded for the entire rest day. Chan told Bookman yesterday; he waited for morning to talk. America has passed a law stopping Chinese workers from going there.

Buck Tooth panicked right away, claiming that Canada will slam its door too, even kick out the Chinese who are already here, people like us. Big Uncle says not to worry because Canada needs workers to build the railway. Gambler asked for wine: he wants to stop thinking.

Everyone has relatives in America. We hear of how the Red Beards want to drive out the Chinese and keep the country for Westerners only. Now America's government is moving in that direction. Cook worries that the police and army will no longer protect the Chinese. Pock Face's granduncle and twenty others were killed about ten years ago when Red Beards attacked the Chinese living in an American city.

We know the Red Beards here do not like us. But we are doing a good job building the railway, aren't we? That makes me sad, to think that no matter how hard we work, the Red Beards still dislike us.

June 20

At breakfast Pock Face came running. "Gone," he panted. "Not moving. He's dead!"

Big Lump was curled into himself, like a child. Big Uncle felt for a pulse. He shook his head and sent everyone out.

"Are you sure?" demanded Mouse, who slept in the same tent. "Could he be sleeping deeply? Could he be getting better right now?"

We carried him to the forest, to a spot near Slant Mouth Bing. Bookman came by, writing in his notebook, so we could not dig as deep. Wong

Brother swore under his breath at Bookman. The rain made the digging even harder.

So far, two men in our crew have died: Slant Mouth Bing and Big Lump. Limp Leg may be dead too, but we are not sure. I went through my journal and counted eight accidents (almost one per week!), but I only recorded the serious ones.

June 21

I counted twenty-six work days since last payday and took care not to spend a single penny on ANYTHING. Still, I didn't get $26, not even before my deductions. A half day was deducted for paying respects to Slant Mouth Bing, for following Boss Chan to Slant Mouth Bing's grave, and for digging Big Lump's grave. When I protested, Bookman replied, "One, you should have paid respects to Slant Mouth Bing on the rest day. Two, no one said you had to walk with Boss Chan. Three, it didn't take twenty men to dig a grave."

"What about Slant Mouth Bing's grave?" I sputtered. "You helped dig that one."

Different deaths, he explained. Slant Mouth Bing died while working, but Big Lump injured himself on his own time.

I hate these bosses. If only the mosquitoes could suck out all their blood. My expenses totalled $12.47

so I earned $13.53, only half of what I had expected. I had no idea how all my daily costs added up!

I hear other men grumbling, but I don't want to discuss my problems with them.

June 22

At breakfast, everyone asked, "Did you hear? Did you hear?"

We all heard a human baby calling. It must have been an animal, for there was no other explanation. On the way to work, we all walked close together.

June 23

On the third day after Big Lump's death, only a few of us watched the candles and incense burn. Cook provided no extra food. We used our own lunches. Wong Brother poured wine. He said just before Big Lump left home, his wife had given birth to a son.

Before we left the grave, Wong Brother handed out coins to everyone there. It was a Canadian 25-cent piece!

"Big Lump was an ordinary man," Wong Brother called out. "Buddha teaches us to be charitable, so both Big Lump and his wife want his life and work to help make your life and work a little easier. If Big Lump owed any of you money, I will be glad to settle the account. And if any of you owed him any money, that debt is hereby cancelled."

We all nodded gratefully. On the way back, Wong Brother told me that Big Lump had good points and bad. These final acts of generosity would smooth his way into the afterlife.

I asked Wong Brother why he had taken this on. Usually it was the deceased's sons who did that.

"Big Lump was my kin," said Wong Brother. "Here, we should all care for one another."

At our clearing, Toothpick lay flat on the ground. His arm was pinned under a heavy tree. They had been rolling it away when it stopped. Toothpick went to see what was underneath. He stuck out his axe and then his hand, and the ground gave way and the tree rolled over his arm.

Big Uncle muttered, "If he had gone to pay respects, he'd be fine right now."

And he would be 25 cents richer too!

We all pushed the trunk, even Crew Boss and Bookman. Luckily, Toothpick's arm had sunk into soft earth.

June 24

Big Uncle was moving a log when it crushed his left foot. This had happened to his right foot before. Now his left toes were bleeding and turning black.

Bookman took Big Uncle's water jug and smashed it against a tree. It was not water, but rice wine. Back at camp, Bookman found more liquor in Big Uncle's tent. He shouted, "Fool, I warned you, drink your wine only on the rest day. If you drink at work, you are a danger to all of us."

He smashed all the jugs on the beach. From the steady way that Big Uncle spoke and worked, I never imagined that liquor affected his judgement.

June 25

I went to the stream. Wong Brother was there, sitting against a tree. He spoke without opening his eyes. "I'm running off soon."

I had nothing to say. He told me he would look for gold upriver. He would look for Seto and Soo.

"Is it so bad here?" I asked, hoping to change his mind. Those two old miners had been here for twenty-two years, and still had not struck gold. How could Wong Brother possibly succeed? I reminded him that if he ran off, then he would lose the wages he had earned.

"No so bad?" he snorted. "People are dying! Getting maimed! The bosses think only of money. Land, sky and water, they hate us too! They entrap us. If we stay, we will die!"

I suddenly saw how very angry he was. It made

me wonder about myself. Why was I not furious about the men's deaths? Because I believed that if I did not like a job, then I should quit. Yet, here Wong Brother wanted to leave, and I did not like it. What was the matter with me? Was I afraid to lose this friend? Or was he afraid of this work?

"I'm no coward," he said, as if he had read my mind. "I cannot die or lose an arm here. No one else in my family can work. Do you understand?"

Of course I did. My earnings were badly needed at home too. I had earned $17.05. Grandfather could use it to get back his store. Too bad it all depended on how fast Ba could repay our debt. I had been furious at Ba and Grandfather's gambling, which had dumped me into this danger. This work wasn't meant for a boy my age! I didn't want to die or be maimed for life! Maybe Wong Brother was right to direct his anger at the bosses. They were the ones standing back and watching us get injured!

Yet I saw things differently. Running away was akin to not paying your bill after eating a meal or buying some goods. Our rice store had seen such customers. We hated them.

June 26

Big Uncle regained his wine last night. Yesterday Watermelon and Mouse trekked to the other camp. They reported that the liquor merchant was there, on his last visit. He is going north, where many new crews recently arrived.

June 27

After dinner tonight, Wong Brother whispered to me that he was leaving tomorrow. He asked me to grab some extra food for him when I went for my lunch food.

I bit my lip, trying to be brave, and yet it was Wong Brother who was more courageous.

June 28

Good news! Wong Brother changed his plans!

At breakfast, Bookman announced the crew was moving. He told us to fold the tents and pack. Money God went to count the tools.

"You are a lucky bunch," said Bookman. "You will ride the fire car on the iron road. Not every worker gets such a chance."

Big Uncle frowned. "Why must we go?" he demanded.

"Company orders." Bookman strutted around and spoke as if addressing little children. "North of Yale, the iron road goes into the mountains, through solid rock. You, you had it easy here, working with trees! The Company needs to lay more iron so the fire car can deliver supplies farther up the line."

"And Slant Mouth Bing and Big Lump?" pressed Big Uncle.

"You want to bring them along?" asked Bookman.

No-one had an answer for that. Later, as we took down the canvas, I asked Wong Brother if he still wanted to run off.

"I want to see the fire car." He grinned.

Me too!

Later, at Yale, British Columbia

On the boat, I suddenly waved and yelled, "Seto Uncle! Seto Uncle!"

But it must have been someone of the Tait band. I felt proud that I could look back in my journal and find the right name for the local people. Wong Brother gave me a funny look. For a moment, I thought he might shout "Rock Brain!"

On the shore, brown-skinned women and children picked bright-coloured berries. Huge baskets hung on their backs. Their laughter reminded me of home, of children playing rock-toss on the street. Mountains pressed in like stern soldiers. We docked at where I had stopped chasing Ba. Fattened cows waited for a boat. We looked hungrily at them.

Workers came aboard and greeted us. On travel days, they told us, we received only half-day wages.

"The bosses made us move," growled Gambler, "so they owe us full wages!"

"But they paid for the transport," said Big Uncle. That sounded fair to me, but Gambler, Little Uncle and Wong Brother cornered Bookman. They demanded full pay, claiming they were ready to do a full day's work right there. Bookman called them idiots. They threatened to throw him into the river. Bookman advised them to talk to Boss Chan. I avoided Wong Brother after that.

Bookman went ashore at Yale while we stayed on the boat. The mosquitoes had followed us from the forest. I kept scratching, even though I knew better.

Yale's mountains plunged from great heights into the river. High up, huge trees sprang from raw rock. The town's wooden shacks were hardly as sturdy as those in the big port where we had landed. But Yale was a hundred times busier, jammed with people, horses and wagons.

A steamer unloaded more workers. Several hundred men went down the gangplank. They were fresh from China: no Western shoes yet.

Bookman returned and grinned sourly. "Your

lucky day," he spat out. "Fire car isn't ready yet. Boss says to set you loose, let you see the town."

Freedom! Away from Bookman and the forest! See a new place! Best of all, I had the coins earned from letter-writing to jingle in my hand!

I hurried to the Chinese stores and asked if anyone had heard of Ba. Gambling occurred at the stores, and I knew that if Ba was working nearby, then for sure he would come here to try his luck. I desperately needed to know if he had been winning or not. But the stores were crowded with customers, and the clerks only pretended to listen before waving me away. At one store, I hid among the customers and did not buy a thing. Being in the store whisked me home with familiar smells: salt fish, flattened ducks, pickled greens, incense, and, best of all, high-quality rice.

The town contained more Nlaka'pamux, Sto:lo, Tait, and Chinese than Red Beards. The people with the golden-brown skin guided long teams of oxen pulling supply wagons. Chinese tended vegetable fields, just like at home. At a door, a beggar held out a tin can. It was Stir-the-Pot! The last time I had seen him, he was standing near Ba, waiting to leave the ship. I called his name and asked what had happened. He held up his right hand and winced in pain. He had no fingers.

"We were sawing a tree," was all he said. "I was careless."

He told me that Ba gambled all the time and still had not regained our wages. Then he looked me in the eyes and said, "If your father had won, for sure he would give me enough to buy a ticket home."

I gave him all my coins and ran to the boat. I ran before I could change my mind and ask him for my money back.

There, I hardly recognized my workmates. Some had visited a barber and had their foreheads shaved and beards removed. Others wore new clothes, after taking hot baths at a laundry. The wise ones bought incense to repel mosquitoes. Wong Brother bought roasted peanuts, and insisted that I take some. I teased him halfheartedly for foolish spending. Then I mentioned my bad news, that Ba and I were still in debt. Wong Brother told me to cheer up.

"You are doing all that you can!" he said, tapping me lightly on the cheek.

I had always wanted an older brother. If I did have one, then he should be exactly like Wong Brother.

June 29

The iron road is not what I expected. Two squarish poles of gleaming steel are laid side by side, as wide as the fire car. The train's wheels perch atop the steel and roll along the tracks, which stretch out as far as the eye can see, around mountains and through tunnels. Very clever! No steel is wasted where the fire car does not touch the ground. The rest of the road is made from wooden ties and gravel. Fire-car wheels are thick iron. A car is so heavy that thirty men could not lift it. Instead, cars are pulled by a coal-burning barrel on even bigger wheels.

We scrambled on. The brave ones sat at the edge and dangled their feet. Others sat in the middle, looking nervously for a handhold.

The ride was smooth but noisy as wheels squealed and the lead car pounded like a blacksmith's shop. Smoke spurted from its chimney. We were barely comfortable with the quick rolling when we suddenly plunged into darkness. The men gasped. The fire car thundered on. The smoke from the lead car choked us. Bookman shouted "Stay calm!"

Then we emerged into fresh air. Tunnels have been dug into these towering mountains. The passages grew longer and longer. I cringed, thinking the weight of the rock above would crush the tunnels. But long worms burrow deep into the earth and always emerge on the surface.

I gasped at the rocky cliffs. The river cut through mountains that rose in vertical walls on both sides of the water. The iron road was being pressed onto the mountain, like a long shelf on a wall. On one side of the track was steep rock. On the other side, rock and gravel sloped to the rushing river. But around the noise and bustle of road-building, Nlaka'pamux people continued to gather berries from thick bushes.

June 30, near Dutchman's Bar, British Columbia

We saw right away that our new Crew Boss does not like us.

From our camp, we walked closer to the mountain, to a gaping dark hole. Chinese hurried out, followed by Nlaka'pamux men and Red Beards. They dropped tin lanterns onto a pile. Then they ran down the line, away from the tunnel. Of course we followed, and crouched behind sturdy trees.

We heard a bang, a sharp thud. Then another one and another. The workers were counting aloud and calling to each other.

"Seven? Was that seven?"

"Couldn't hear. I'm deaf from all this noise."

Smoke billowed from the tunnel. We took lanterns in, dropping them here and there to mark a path through the dark. We used shovels, baskets and carrying-poles to clear the rubble. When a rock was too big for a basket, we roped it up and slung it between two men. Boulders that were too heavy to move got stuffed with black powder to be exploded again.

The Red Beards drilled holes into the mountain and filled them with blasting powder. Along with the constant cursing and coughing, the work was very noisy. A man held a drill rod in the rock while another man stood back and swung his hammer at the drill. With each hit, the rod was rotated a bit before the next hammer blow. From time to time, the pairs of men switched positions.

The light was so dim that I could not see how many men were at the rock face, some high on ladders, others kneeling. The ground was strewn with rubble: one slip and you could twist your ankle. In the tight space, the dust floated and thickened. If the man swung his hammer and missed the drill, then he would shatter his partner's arm. The bone would explode into a million little splinters and never be healed. Spellbound, I watched. It was hard to imagine men working so hard at so ungiving a job. To throw men and axes against giant trees was nothing compared to throwing men and puny little drills against a mountain! It was hard to tear myself away, yet when I left, I breathed a sigh of relief. What a coward I am!

Crew Boss chewed tobacco and spat out, usually at our feet. Our first crew boss never watched us. He came by once or twice a day and that was all. Bookman snooped around to see who was lazy.

Watermelon staggered out of the tunnel, coughing from the dust. He ran to drink water. Crew Boss ripped the scooper from his hand, shoved him to the ground and overturned the pail. He cuffed him around the head. Watermelon was dazed and bleeding. We came running. Bookman shouted at Watermelon, "You stupid fool! That water is for the Red Beards. *Your* water is over there."

The tunnel mouth is a narrow jumble of rock, tools and machines. Red Beards loiter there, waiting for us to remove the rock so that they can reenter to drill and blast. We work in two lines. The one leaving the tunnel is by the mountainside, away from the drop to the river below.

A man came out of the tunnel and fell. He may have tripped over the foot of a Red Beard. He sprawled across the path and rubble spilled from his baskets. He cursed loudly. Buck Tooth was going the other way, with empty baskets. He avoided the spill but fell backwards and tumbled down to the river. We threw down a long rope to help him climb back up.

An accident is not a good sign on a first day.

July 1

Canada's birthday is a rest day. It is fifteen years old. How strange to mark a country's birth, as if it were a person. I guess it is the same as Teacher Chen teaching us that Emperor Qin unified China two thousand years ago. That makes China one hundred and thirty times older than Canada! Teacher Chen also says that before Emperor Qin, China had another two thousand years of history. That total is too big to imagine. Would that make eighty levels of grandfathers?

Red Beards yelled and sang drunkenly last night. Someone played a stringed instrument; it sounded like a cat yowling in pain. The Red Beards barged through our camp, stomping their feet, chanting jauntily and waving torches. They crashed into our clotheslines and tore them down. We cursed them and stood ready to fight if they should try to set our tents on fire. But they ran off.

A braggart from the other Chinese crew came to chat. When we mentioned doing forest clearing, he smirked and called it women's work.

Rock work was much harder, he declared. When he heard that all Chinese workers got the same pay, he insisted rock workers deserved twice as much.

Big Uncle told him how the forest had claimed many lives. The fellow sneered. "They must have been stupid," he said.

Big Uncle almost hit him.

Later, more men from that crew visited. They told us to ignore Ah-Bee, the braggart from earlier. "He thinks he is smarter than everyone else."

Broken Bowl, Lucky and Fur Melon had been here two months. They also disliked their crew boss. The Company pressed for work to speed up, they said, to open more tunnels. This one was Tunnel #12. Other crews were working on it too, digging toward us from the other side. I thought of two boats sailing toward each other during a moonless night. What if the two crews missed each other?

Big Uncle said he was surprised that simple hand tools were being used to drill through the massive mountain. "It will take forever," he exclaimed. "Don't the Red Beards have machines?"

Lucky said there was much talk about using machines to advance the work, but nothing ever arrived. Instead, he said the Red Beards count on humans. We are flesh and bone, so they do not need an expert to figure out how to get us to work.

We asked, "Is there gold in the river here?"

No, said Broken Bowl, it flows too fast. He was right. Two days ago, we had left the fire car when the iron road ended. We trekked by the river, on a path crowded with wagons, cattle, horses and oxen. Dust choked us. To cross the river, we boarded a raft. Long ropes at both ends let workers on the other shore pull us across.

"Don't go into the river," Broken Bowl said. "The current can drag you off; no one will know you're gone."

Six tunnels were underway in this area, said Fur Melon, so plenty of workers lived nearby. Chinese merchants had set up stores, but if any worker shopped at a non-Company store, then his daily pay was cut to 80 cents. Nobody liked this, but Old Uncle had a joke.

> Two travellers meet on the road to Hong Kong. When night comes, they stop at an inn. While waiting for rooms, they look in their bags and take out rice dumplings to eat. The innkeeper serves meals too, so he declares, "You cannot eat your own food here."

> The two travellers glance at one another. Then each man hands his dumpling to the other, and both calmly continue eating.

It felt wonderful to laugh again.

July 2

Every seventh day is for rest. I forgot during the move. Two rest days in a row are a luxury. I wanted to find a stream for fishing, and cool off a bit from the heat. But Bookman handed me two shirts. He had bought them in Yale, and wanted them starched to stay new. "Go to the wash house," he said.

Was there one here? Bookman told me to find the shack with clothes drying outside.

"I don't speak Red Beard language," I protested. Nor was I his servant.

"You fool," he said. "The wash house man is Chinese."

Fung was surprised to see me. "Chinese people wash their own clothes," he explained. "Only Red Beards bring their dirty clothes. They think washing clothes is women's work."

True, I thought. At home, Ma or the women servants did that chore.

"Earlier, I worked on the iron road," Fung

added. "But I earn more here. Better yet, I wake up and never worry about dying on the job."

Then a delicious smell hit me. Pork, steamed with black beans! Fung invited me to stay, and I accepted greedily. His helper brought soup, greens and bowls of rice. I had not tasted pork since leaving the ship! Afterwards, I thanked my host and vowed to bring him a fresh fish.

July 3

No work for us today. Will this mean no pay?

Bookman laughed when someone asked him that same question. "You think the Company pays you for sitting around?" chortled Bookman. "You are dreaming!"

But we were ready to work, so we should get paid. No pay is bad news, but Bookman did not have to make us feel stupid for asking. How are we supposed to know the rules if no one tells them to us? I do not like this job, but I do not like being idle either!

This morning, the Red Beard bosses huddled with our bookmen. While we checked our baskets for damage, Bookman came and said, "No work today. No blasters."

On Canada's birthday, the Red Beards had gone to Yale, to a grand celebration. They still had not returned. We hoped they were on their way and wondered why they did not care about their pay. Did they not have debts, like us? Bookman told us that last year there were so many mosquitoes that the Red Beards all quit and stayed in Yale until the muddy swamps dried up. Finally, Toothpick lost his patience, jumped to his feet and offered to go drill the rock. Money God offered to join him, saying that drilling did not look difficult to do. But Bookman reminded us that we were not paid to do that work.

I guess we should celebrate. Three days of rest. It is like the New Year!

July 4

New Red Beard workers went into the tunnel. We were waiting outside when we heard a boom. But the Red Beards had not come out. The crew bosses eyed one other and paced about anxiously but did not go in. After a while, two men staggered out, one supporting the other. Their faces and hands were covered with black soot.

Bookman told us the powder exploded before it should have. A Red Beard got badly burned, and his hands were shattered. Bookman warned us, if we ever saw the Red Beards using blasting powder while we were inside, then we should run out as fast as we could.

Old Uncle shook his head. "Those men don't know what they're doing."

"Everyone has to learn," replied Bookman.

July 5

More Red Beards arrived and a new boss pushed us to make up the lost time. Under his orders, our first job after an explosion is to clear the rubble that blocks his workers from reaching the rock face. Then his men could drill as we cleared the remaining debris. Bookman assured us the Red Beards would only drill and never use black powder when we were around.

We were nervous and moved faster, but then Crew Boss accused us of taking lighter loads. He and Bookman argued loudly. Crew Boss wanted us to empty our baskets into the river, but Bookman ordered the debris be used to fill a gully down the line.

We look like bandits, with cloth wrapped around our heads to hide our noses. The explosions release thick clouds of dust that the winds hurl into our faces. We narrow our eyes and squint as much as possible. As we breathe, our noses and throats feel dry and cracked. Once you start coughing, it is hard to stop. But the cloth makes us sweat even more. When we get back to camp, everyone rushes to fetch water to bathe and to flush the grit out of our throats.

July 7

We thought the danger lay inside the tunnel but it hovered outside too. Rocks hurtled down the mountain and crashed into us. The narrow path slowed our escape. A man from Lucky's crew was slow, and his legs were crushed. He screamed in pain, but no one could relieve him. His workmates carried him to the raft to send him to a doctor. Then we cleared the outside path before going back into the tunnel. It is a living death to lose one's legs. Can you imagine being stuck in one place, all day long, watching people walk and skip by you, laughing and talking and going places you will never see?

July 9

Wong Brother and I went fishing but he said very little. The narrow path at work forces us to walk single file. If Wong Brother is not right ahead or right behind me, then we cannot talk, even when we stand and wait for Red Beards to come out.

We went up a side stream into the forest. We crashed through bushes and found two Red Beards, fishing with long poles. They looked at us, and then went on talking softly as we went farther upriver.

Wong Brother asked if I wished Ba were in this crew. I told him honestly that I didn't know, because we argued so often. Wong Brother reminded me what Ba had said to Sell-Ginger on the boat. Yes, Ba had spoken well, but then I reminded Wong Brother that Ba's gambling was hurting our family.

Some nights, I stare for hours into the dark, worrying that Ba and I could be stranded here and never go home to China. After a long pause, Wong Brother told me, "Good-hearted men gamble too."

But that made me think more of Grandfather than Ba.

When we took fish to the laundry, Fung asked us if we could take his assistant Jong fishing. I offered him my line and hook, but Fung refused. He tapped his forehead.

"Jong is lucky to be alive," Fung said. "Have you heard of Hang Halfway from Heaven?"

He told me Jong and his crew went to drill blasting holes at a high cliff. The mountain was tough; it refused to give. Finally, the crew climbed to the top and the boss lowered men down the mountain face. Dangling from thick ropes, the men drilled holes, stuffed blasting powder, and lit long fuses. Then men at the top pulled with all their might to haul them up. But Jong's rope got tangled in a little tree growing out of a crack in the cliff. Jong was chopping at it when the blast went off. Rocks careened into him but the explosion also freed his rope. The men pulled him up, and found him senseless. Now he cannot work or speak. He can only do simple things, like fetch water.

I thought he was just quiet. I promised to take him fishing next time.

July 10

Last night I had a nightmare. I dreamt I was dangling like Jong from a long rope down the face of a cliff. Suddenly eagles attacked. Screeching loudly, their talons clawed at me. I kicked at them and tried to fight them off with my hammer, but they were too fast. They came so close I could see their glinting eyes and smell a fierce odour. I shouted at the crew to haul me up, but they shouted back to keep working. I felt pain in my leg. I looked down. It was bleeding. Then pain erupted in my arm. The eagle had torn away my sleeve and raked into me. But the blood that spurted out was not red. It was black and green. That was when I woke up in a cold sweat.

Today I wrote a letter for Wong Brother but wished he had paid someone else. He addressed his father with respect. He described the accidents of the last while as well as meeting Jong. He wept to admit his father was right. Back home, the father had declared Wong Brother could not do this job or survive the setting. Wong Brother said, "I know now that you do not think I am weak or cowardly. You knew the iron road was no life for any man." Wong Brother wiped his tears and told me to write, "Yet so many of our people are here! How can we live like animals?"

At the end, he made me promise never to tell anyone about this letter.

July 11

More rocks and boulders rolled down on us. The rumbling made us scatter, but no one knew where the rocks would land. Those near the tunnel ran inside. Others rushed down the line. Those caught in the middle flattened themselves against the wall and covered their skulls with pails, hoping the rocks would shoot over their heads. Luckily, no one was hit. We demanded better protection. We use the path all the time, coming and going from the tunnel. We cleared the outside debris as fast as we could.

July 12

No more fresh vegetables. We ate the last of the greens brought up from Yale.

July 14

More rocks roll down the mountain. People say heavy rains are loosening the rocks higher up.

July 16

It rained and we could not go fishing. Nor could we rest. The rain collected atop our sagging tents in heavy pools. We had to release the water before the roof collapsed on us. Then we dug long trenches to take the water away from us. It was supposed to be a rest day, but it felt more like a work day! At least the rain cooled the air. Water falling on dry bush releases a pungent smell, a bit like straw baking in the paddy fields that suddenly gets wet.

Wong Brother spent the day in the gamblers' tent. I never thought he was the gambling type. I said nothing, to avoid having him call me "woman" like Ba did.

July 18

The bosses decided to put an end to the rocks rolling onto the iron road path. They sent men up the mountain to blast it. Mid-morning, from afar, we heard explosions, one after another and another. When we headed back, the iron road path was buried under rocks, timber and boulders, all tangled three storeys high.

Skinny and lightweight, I climbed the heap of rubble first. At the top, I waved triumphantly. I could see more of the other side of the riverbank. The men shouted at me to get to work. I threw down rocks and gingerly tugged at pieces around me. Every little rattle made me think the heap would fall apart, drop me into its centre, and crush me dead.

July 20

Little Uncle was near the top of the rubble heap when he yanked at something and lost his footing. Sliding down, he loosened more debris. Everyone backed off as he slammed into the ground. Then a table-sized rock rolled onto him. We called to him but he was silent. By the time we lifted the rock, he had stopped breathing. Crew Boss ordered us to remove him, so we thought to bury him. Crew Boss stopped us. We had to bury Little Uncle after our shift.

It was hard to find a spot because the mountain had little flat land. Lucky told us that the Nlaka'pamux people stored their dead in boxes high in the trees. We asked what his crew had done with their bodies. He said they had buried them by the river. He shrugged, knowing the river would rise and carry them away.

"We are Wongs," Money God said, "We treat

our people with respect. If we need to walk all the way around this mountain, we will."

Lucky felt insulted, and left us. "Watch out for wildcats," he said. "They devour humans."

Three new crew members, who are not Wongs, stayed with us. In fact, they carried the pickaxes and heavy shovels.

I felt guilty. If we had not backed away when Little Uncle tumbled down, he would still be alive. If we had quickly yanked him away, then that rock would have missed him. Please, Little Uncle, forgive me.

I remembered Little Uncle from our very first day at work, and it almost made me cry. He and Buck Tooth brought down the second tree of the day, and then another one. They were the only men who managed to chop down two towering trees in one day. That night, Little Uncle and Buck Tooth grinned endlessly. The men in our crew do not smile as much now.

I looked around for Buck Tooth tonight, but he had walked away from the camp. Everyone was sad. Everyone liked Little Uncle. He wasn't afraid of anything.

July 21

Payday. I have worked seventy-one days, but instead of $71 I have $28.13. This month, I bought a shirt, a hat and underpants. On travel days, we only get 50 cents a day. And on the day the Red Beards did not work, we only got half a day's pay.

Worse, a Company note stating that my wages were promised to someone else had been inserted into the ledger. Bookman was warned not to advance me any large sums. Good thing I had not asked for an advance in Yale. He would have laughed heartily at me.

I can only hope that Ba's luck at gambling has improved since Stir-the-Pot saw him. I never cheer on gamblers because Ma and I both believe that gambling is a loser's game. But here I have no choice but to pray for Ba to play his way out of this disaster.

July 22

I was atop the rubble heap when I heard whimpering sounds. Crew Boss held Jong and gave him short tight slaps. A pail of water lay overturned at their feet. I shouted at Crew Boss to stop, but he didn't understand Chinese. I needed something to hurl, but nothing was nearby. No one was around. Jong finally broke free and ran off.

Pock Face came at the day's end and asked me to read a letter from his wife. Good news! The matchmaker found a boy from a good family for their daughter! They have already traded small gifts. Pock

Face jumped up and gave me double my reading fee. Then he rushed around the camp, spreading his good news. It's a relief to see his limp is gone.

July 23

Jong came to me, early, wanting to go fishing, but this was the third day after Little Uncle's death. I wanted to apologize for not helping Jong yesterday, but kept quiet. Maybe he had not seen me up on the rubble heap.

Back at camp, Wong Brother said he hated this work and wanted to run away. I said nothing.

Pock Face told me to write to his wife, telling her not to wait for his return but to set their daughter's wedding for as early as possible. Without thinking, I asked how he could miss the wedding. He grinned and said that when he went home, he wanted to hold his first grandchild!

July 25

The Red Beards are smiling. Two good reasons! Big drills powered by fire and steam have arrived. As well, we finished clearing the outside rubble so they can enter the tunnel and work. They do not get paid for standing around and waiting. Clearing the rubble is hard, but at least we work in the daylight and fresh air.

The tunnel is badly lit, so you cannot see the ground. You only know that if you fall, it is very painful if not deadly. The louder and faster drilling causes ever more dust to fly everywhere, so you want to shut your eyes. But you need to see the way.

The Red Beards work the drills by boiling water in a tank and sending steam through long snakes to the men inside. Some of Lucky's men work beside the drillers, carrying the equipment out when it is time to blast. They think it is the best job, because they stand around and wait and get paid. And they think they are safe, because of course the Red Beards will protect themselves.

Wong Brother has not run away. That is good.

July 26

The Red Beards stopped smiling. Last night the roof collapsed and clogged the tunnel with debris. The men are muttering that the new machine drills must have shaken the mountain too much, and caused the ceiling to break apart. Worst of all, the Red Beards left their new equipment at the rock face. The falling rocks may have destroyed it. What a waste that would be. We will clear the rubble but no one knows how long it will take. The Red Beards are leaving but the Nlaka'pamux and other local people are staying to work with us.

The debris in the tunnel is the same as that which killed Little Uncle. We see but do not want to speak about it. We work carefully. Crew Boss glares at us, but we pay him no attention.

July 28

Crashing sounds suddenly boomed through the tunnel. The ground shook beneath our feet, and I thought it would open up and swallow us. We sprinted out the entrance and hid in the bushes. After a while, we heard the birds chirping in the trees around us. When we inched into the tunnel, we discovered more of the ceiling had collapsed, but farther inside.

July 29

We came back from the gully, and Crew Boss was teasing a little Nlaka'pamux girl. He had taken her basket and held it high, just beyond her reach. When she lunged for it, he jerked it away. When she jumped for it, he stepped back. The little girl's face was dark with anger, but she refused to cry out. Finally, I ran up behind Crew Boss, grabbed the basket, and handed it back to the girl.

July 30

We went fishing but caught nothing. Jong cannot sit still. We removed our boots at the stream, but when it came time to leave, I couldn't find mine. They had stood right beside Jong's. I hobbled back home, leaning on Jong and walking in the river. I knew who had stolen them. Crew Boss had seen us leave camp, so he must have followed.

I asked Bookman to recover my boots.

"Where's your proof?" he demanded. "Whoever took them may have thrown them into the river. Or high into a tree. Go buy a new pair. You want to fight Crew Boss, but what's the use? He could refuse to approve your wages."

Bookman offered to take me to the Company store tomorrow. But I would lose a day's wages! I felt my fist clenching and unclenching, but there was little I could do. If Wong Brother was running away tonight, I would go with him. But I would need boots first.

Gambler and Pock Face each had kept one good boot from their forest accidents. Luckily, there was one boot for each of my feet between them. They let me wear the boots but they fit badly: one was loose and the other was too tight. But I could not afford to lose a day's pay.

July 31

Bad shoes are bad news. The bigger one stubbed the ground and down I went, with two baskets of debris. My palms were bloodied and my knees felt shattered. One knee was very soft and I could barely walk on it, even after tying my sweat rag around it. I saw Crew Boss sneering at me, and that made me return to work.

August 2

Rocks dropped from the ceiling and struck Mouse. His shoulder was bruised but he could still work. A man from Lucky's crew suffered badly: a sharp rock sheared off his ear.

Wong Brother and I went to relieve ourselves. He asked me to run off with him, again. When I hesitated, he labelled me a coward. He said I feared the forest, Company agents, and starving to death. I reminded him that an honest man always repaid his debts. Then I called him an idiot for chasing after gold. Seto and Soo were still poor as dirt. What kind of a life was that?

He stomped off. I wanted to hurl one of my boots at his head. But then, "Don't run off!" burst out of me in a childish wail, which I did not intend. Writing this down makes me look like a baby, but I must be honest.

It made Wong Brother stop, and he came back, peering at me curiously. He tried again to get me to run off with him. But I yelled at him for being afraid to die on the job, for being too scared to fail at this work. He shook his head sadly and said, "You don't think it takes courage to do what I'm doing?"

When he walked away, I felt like a three-year-old. Later, I wondered if it was possible for both of us to be right at the same time and still not see eye to eye?

August 3

Loud shouting arose from the Red Beards' camp last night. We heard sharp cracks. In the morning, we learned a bear had been prowling around their camp. Someone had shot a deer, which the cook had cleaned and cooked. But the bear smelled blood and came looking for food. It ran away when a Red Beard fired a gun. The bear tracks looked like human footprints, but much wider. The past few days have been hot, so the deer meat must be spoiling quickly.

This dry heat is unlike what we have at home. There, the sticky warmth of summer has us dripping from human sweat and soggy air. Here, our skin stays dry, except for where sweat pours out.

Some men work without shirts, and get darker and darker each day. Too bad we did not bring our wide-brimmed straw hats from home. They would have been helpful. The tunnel is dark and cool, but as soon as we step into the bright sunlight, we feel the heat and look for the water bucket. The sun is fiercely hot, as are the exposed faces of rock. The mountains are thick with forest, but the trees are too far away to give us any shade.

August 5

We finished clearing the way to the rock face. No-one expected it could be done so quickly. The bosses were especially happy that the drilling machines had not been damaged.

Wong Brother has not run away yet. Maybe he fears bears.

August 6

We went to the Company store. Fung the washman knew the way and talked to the raft-men. On the road, many horse-drawn wagons clattered past, but none offered us a ride. Across the river, we saw the iron road taking shape. Sides of the mountain had been sliced off, leaving great bald spots in the rock and fresh debris in the river. The tents looked tiny and flimsy.

My feet were hurting, so I prayed the store was not too far. The man who lost his ear came too, to ask the Chinese contractor if he could go home. Wong Brother came too. I thought he might take advantage and run off.

We crossed the river again. The store was at Tunnel #6, a very long one. It needed so many workers that the camp was called Tunnel City. The Company had offices and a machine shop there. Fung said families lived there too, and sure enough, we saw children scampering around, playing games. The largest buildings were boarding houses for the Red Beard workers. They did not live in tents like us! Fung saw friends who ran a wash house there.

In the store, my boots cost $5 – almost a week's wages! Fung said that in a regular store, they would cost $2. Wong Brother shouted at the Chinese clerk, "You lazy snake. You hide behind the counter and suck blood from your own people. We are dying in the mountains while you drink your fill here. Do you sleep well at night?"

I ran from the store as fast as I could go.

August 8

One of Lucky's crew men lost an eye today. He was working with a Red Beard, drilling at the rock face. A small piece of rock flew out and went right into his eye. He was so scared that he wept and howled, but that only worsened his pain. It makes me cold to think of losing an eye. I would rather lose a finger or an arm, or even a leg, rather than give up my eye. With explosions, you can never tell what will happen.

August 10

Cook ran out of rice. Supplies failed to arrive a few days ago. He mixed flour with water and made soggy cakes. They tasted horrible.

August 12

Still no rice. Cook boiled up Western potatoes, which had no taste and no texture. Someone hurled one at Cook's back, leaving a pulpy smear on his shirt.

August 13

The rain ruined my plans for fishing. I wanted to get away from Wong Brother's moping. At the laundry, Fung and Jong had a visitor. I offered to leave, but Fung was serving fresh-cooked food: fish with ginger, and eggs with tomatoes. Of course I stayed. The visitor enjoyed the meal and spoke to me with the help of Fung's translations. He asked my age because I looked so young. I thought I looked older from not washing my face regularly. He told me he was from the Tait people. He asked what my family did in China. He told me to open a rice shop nearby because his people liked rice.

August 14

We broke through the rock today. Two Chinese crews danced through from the other side. We held up lanterns, to see each others' faces. Gambler grabbed someone and started talking, only to find that it was a Red Beard.

We went through to the other mouth. It was no different from our side. The ground was just as littered, so we knew that the other Chinese were not neater than us. When we strolled back, it felt magical to walk in just one direction and go from light to darkness and back to light. It seemed like we were actually going far away. Usually we had to turn around, to return to the light at the start. Here, it was as if we had done something important. In the forest, we could never chop down enough trees to make the path. Here, even Wong Brother looked cheerful.

People shared jugs of rice wine. They asked for surnames and home districts, trying to find persons they knew. How wonderful, to travel around the world and meet someone who lives downstream from you. Too bad I knew no-one.

August 15

We were folding our tents when I remembered the laundry. Fung was not packing because Red Beard workers would arrive to do a month's work here.

"And after that?" I asked. "Where will you go then?"

He could not follow us because someone already had a laundry near the next camp. He and Jong might try gold mining or trek south to work in the fish canneries. He explained that factory men put fresh fish into tin cans, sealed them with molten metal, and then cooked the tins. Afterwards, the fish never spoiled, and were shipped around the world. He told me the rivers would soon teem with spawning fish.

I wished him and Jong a safe journey. Heading back to camp, I wiped tears off my face. Heaven would protect Fung because he took such care of Jong.

August 17

The new site was the same: mountain on one side, river on the other. The path was no wider, so we could not work faster even if we wanted to. The

Red Beard drillers and blasters were new. They arrived two days ago, so plenty of rock needed to be moved.

During yesterday's trek, we climbed over a hill and everyone gasped. The cliffs ahead of us formed a wall across the river, squeezing it through a narrow gap. Behind the rock, the river was wide and deep; its trapped water churned through in an angry froth.

Supply boats would never get past this. The current was too strong and the rocks were too dangerous. The boat would be hurled back, or smashed into pieces. We groaned and thought of rice shortages again. Cook told us not to worry. Supplies would be hauled farther north on the wagon road, and then moved across the river where waters were calmer. He said to worry more about bears in this area.

August 18

Yesterday's drillers and blasters were new workers. Now they are dead, along with Money God.

Crew Boss had complained the work was slow and urged his men to drill faster. Inside, we saw Money God crouched by the machine, stroking it as if it were a family pet. Was he trying to fix it? Then came a terrible explosion.

No other Chinese were near the blast. When

the bodies were brought out, their pale faces were streaked with black powder, blood and rock fragments.

After dinner, Wong Brother spoke to me. His eyes were glassy and red, as if they had been rubbed with a dirty cloth. "I'm going," he whispered, "this time for sure! Will you grab extra food from breakfast for me?"

I nodded. He handed me five pencils.

"Farewell gift," he said. "Your pencils are almost used up, and you're too careful with your own money."

"I can buy my own pencils," I insisted. If he had bought me a gift ahead of time, then he was serious about leaving.

"Keep writing letters for the others," he said.

August 22

I am so sick, I am dying. My head pounds. My ribs ache from coughing. I have no energy. My feet will not hold me up. My stomach hurts. I force myself to chew and swallow. I need to be strong and get back to work. I have lost four days of wages.

August 31

I thought I was getting better. Instead, I get worse. My body heats up. My clothes and blankets drip with my sweat. I fling away my blankets, but someone replaces them. When I squat in the woods, waste flows out in a thick stream, sometimes green, sometimes yellow. My stomach is puffed up and tender.

I float through nightmares. At one point, I shout at Wong Brother, "Are you still here, coward? I thought you ran away! Not enough backbone?"

Fung from the laundry, his face moves in and out of focus. What is he doing here? Isn't he heading south? Then I taste bitter tea.

Bookman comes through, slapping our faces and shouting, "Is this man really sick, or is he pretending? How can so many workers get sick at the same time?"

I hear my voice calling out for Ma. How embarrassing. What a baby I am.

September 8

After two weeks, I can stand without shaking. I carry light loads. Cook needs lots of dry firewood to boil all our drinking water.

I went to the river and walked into the water. The sudden cold gave me a shock. A small boat passed. Its passengers were too far away, but their faces were dark ones, maybe Chinese or Nlaka'pamux or Tait. I waved and they saluted me with their oars. I wished I was free to go far away.

Wong Brother said half of our crew sickened in one night: running to the woods, squatting and moaning as they clutched their stomachs, stumbling over logs and bashing their shins and heads. It was hard, he laughed, to tell if people's pain came from nighttime crashes or from the illness. Gambler and Pretty Boy, who were not sick, quickly left with their belongings and their earnings.

The Red Beards were just as sick. The work slowed to a trickle. "It was much safer to work," Wong Brother said with a grin. "I enjoyed myself!"

"Weren't you about to run off?" I asked.

"How could I go?" he retorted. "We thought you were dying!"

The Chinese contractor rode his horse from Tunnel City to visit. He brought packets of herbal teas. Cook boiled it and everyone drank, but no one felt better.

September 9

Today was my first full day of work. I felt weak and was glad to rest next day. Bookman told us a fire car finishing a delivery would then head to Tunnel City.

We could catch a ride. But we would need to make our own way back. AND NOT BE LATE! A group of us want to go, including Old Uncle and Lucky's crew. I need new clothes. My shirts and pants are threadbare and ragged. Worse, no amount of washing can remove the disgusting smells of vomit.

I was sick on payday and I felt ill again when Bookman talked to me today. My pay for the previous month was only $3.35! $1.50 was deducted for two days of travel and for the half a day when we breached the tunnel and did not work. I bought boots, pants, socks, notebook and pencils (before Wong Brother gave me more), and contributed to the funeral fund. Since the start of work, I have earned $31.48. It is a lot of money in China, but when I hear that the Red Beards earn twice as much as us, then I think it is very unfair. Is $30 enough to clear Ba's gambling debt? I wish he had told me how big the debt was. Then I wouldn't worry so much.

On payday, at least one person will ask me to write a letter, so I will make some money. I hope everyone wants to write home about being sick.

September 10

The train went through our tunnel, #12, but I did not recognize it. The road had been built up and levelled, so the fire car ran smoothly and high off the ground. Where did so much earth and gravel come from? Did the Company use machines or workers? I wished I had seen the work.

At Tunnel City, I was happy to bump into Fung. He and Jong had found work here. Fung asked if I recalled his visit when I was sick.

"You!" I exclaimed. "You fed me that bitter tea!"

"I fed it to Red Beards too." Fung laughed. "They were so sick that they were good customers."

Shirts cost $1.75 each. Trousers were $1.75. Socks were 40 cents. In the ledger, I saw the Company had deducted money for more herbal tea from Contractor. Fah! They were useless drinks! Fung said that at a regular store, my clothes would have cost half of what I paid.

Big Uncle needed boots but there was trouble. "You've bought too many things, old man," the clerk said. "Even if you worked another year without ever getting sick, you would still owe us money."

"I need boots." Big Uncle's shoes had gaping holes. He had mended them with tin pieces, but they cut his foot and the leather.

"You should be careful buying things," snapped the clerk, slamming the account book.

"I'll pay for them," said Fung, throwing down some bills. And then he stomped out. Big Uncle went after him, thanking him and promising to repay him.

Wong Brother's face was dark. "We should burn down this store!" he hissed.

We dragged him away as fast as possible.

September 12

The drill that gets its power from steam was broken so we had free time, waiting between blasts. Not until late in the afternoon did another Red Beard arrive to fix it.

September 14

New workers came to replace the ones we had lost. One was assigned to our tent. He washed his shirt and hung it inside to dry. Wong Brother told him to take it outside.

"Tonight it's going to rain," retorted the newcomer. "How will my shirt dry?"

"People wash on the rest day, when there's enough day time to get it dry."

"You people stink," he muttered. From then on, his name was Fragrance.

September 16

Rocks fell from the tunnel's roof. They hit several people, including me, on their arms and shoulders.

Luckily, no one's head got hurt. We waited a while to see if more rock might fall, and then we went back to work. My shoulder is still sore. Good thing I do not have to work tomorrow.

September 17

Bookman said to Wong Brother and me, "You two like to fish? Come with me." We walked along with him. "Look at the water," said Bookman. "See anything?"

No, it was too dark.

We followed a stream that flowed into the main river. Big fish were fighting their way upstream. Their skin was green and red, odd colours for fish. Something did not look right. Their bodies were swollen and puffy, as if they were sick. At a small waterfall, the fish flung themselves out of the water, trying to jump over the ledge to the higher water. It looked as if they were flying! Farther up the river, the waters were thick with dark red fish, twisting and writhing.

Bookman explained that these fish returned to their birthplace after living four years in the ocean. They came back to give birth.

"Why are you showing us this?" I asked. Bookman was never friendly.

"Because Gold Mountain is also about birth and life, not just death."

September 19

Heavy rocks dropped from the roof of the tunnel, near the rock face. They just missed Wong Brother and me. But other men were not so lucky. A slab of rock flattened one Red Beard driller, folded him over like a piece of paper. Another Red Beard driller had his head cracked open. Their Chinese helper died too, crushed under several boulders. I saw so much blood and gore that I threw up over and over.

We did not pull out their bodies right away, worrying about falling rocks. Finally Crew Boss went in with a lantern on a long pole. He poked at the ceiling and said it was safe. We went in quietly. We avoided the noisy gravel, trying not to bang into one another, fearful that the slightest sound would bring down more rocks. Many of us were mumbling prayers to the gods and ancestors.

That night, no one said much as we ate dinner. When I looked at Wong Brother, he shook his head sadly.

September 20

Yesterday, three people were killed in a single day. Last month, two people were killed in one day. With these numbers rising, I fear I may die at any moment. Will I pass into eternal darkness, or into great brightness? Will I still be able to watch my friends at work, or will I be taken far away?

When I awoke this morning, I did not want to go to work. I wanted to burrow deep into my blankets and stay warm and safe. I miss Ma and Grandfather, and (I never thought I would say this) even that pesky Little Brother of mine.

September 21

What a horrible month. I spent more than what I earned. This breaks the rule at our family store: Always take in more money than what you spend! Here, the Company deducted food as if I were eating full meals even when I was deathly sick. I have never known of a firm that is so nasty and miserable. I complained loudly, but Bookman said the Company had promised to provide food on each day of work. Whether or not a worker ate his share, well, that was not the Company's concern. I wanted to kick Bookman!

Medicine and new clothes cost me $13.65, against earnings of $9. Now I own even less money than last month. If this continues, then Ba's gambler friend can't take much. Hurrah, I think. The gambler will lose his loan! What a stupid man!

Then a flash of insight hit me. What if the gambler isn't stupid? What if he knows that railway work is awful and earnings are low? Then he would have lent Ba a small sum! Maybe our debt isn't too high. At least not as bad as Grandfather's debt, where we lost our entire store.

September 22

Life can change so quickly.

Today, we went back to the place Bookman called Hell's Gate. The Company had built a steamboat, called *Skuzzy*, to deliver supplies north of Hell's Gate. But first the boat had to get through the angry waters of the gate.

For six months, the Company had hired veteran sailors and captains to steer the boat through. They all failed. Now the Company told us to *pull* the boat through.

Crews of Chinese waited on both sides of the river. The boat circled below. Its chimney poured out smoke. Its paddlewheel spun in frenzy. We grabbed long heavy ropes that stretched from the boat to the two shores.

The boat took a run at Hell's Gate. Just as the current started pushing it back, bookmen shouted "Pull!"

We pulled. We struggled to get a foothold on the

slippery rocks. The boat did not budge, as if the river gods clutched it firm and were testing us.

The rope was stretched hard as rock, and wet from river spray and our sweat. Our hands struggled to get a firm grip. Someone shouted out a count, so we could merge our efforts.

"One! Two! Three! Pull!"

We gained an inch! A cheer went up. The man shouted out the numbers again, and we gained another inch.

The man in front of me fell. But he hauled himself up and resumed pulling, right on the count, without missing a beat.

Step by step we moved ahead. We waited for the count and threw the weight of our bodies onto our ropes.

"Don't look behind!" shouted Bookman. "Watch your feet!"

We pulled and yanked with all our might. We cursed the river. We wanted to show the Red Beards that we Chinese would succeed where they had failed. We cursed the Company. "It should get a lighter boat!" someone shouted.

Red was streaming from my hands. I can't be bleeding, I thought, my palms are thick as leather! No, the blood came from the man in front, from his fall.

And then it was over. The Red Beards shouted happily, threw their hats into the air, and shook each others' hands.

To send us back to work, the bosses herded us onto *Skuzzy*. Someone called me. It was Ba! He grabbed me and pulled me close.

"Look how big he is!" Poy Uncle exclaimed. "He'll bring you good luck!"

That was bad news. If Ba needed good luck, then he had not regained our wages. I felt uneasy, the same way I felt whenever he came home from overseas. The family would be excited, and Ma's face lit up. But Ba spent no time with me and Little Brother.

Ba called together his bookman and my bookman. They decided I would switch crews. No one asked for my view. If I had blurted, "No, I don't want to go," then Ba would have lost face. I saw Ox Uncle from the ship, and still disliked him. He walked with a limp. Another man wore a hardened scar that jagged across his forehead, nose and cheek. I wondered if this crew had worse luck than my group with work accidents.

The boat chugged to our camp, and I hurried to get my belongings. Wong Brother's blankets and clothes had vanished. When I said goodbye to the crew, Wong Brother did not appear. This time, he really had left.

I felt bad. I had not said goodbye to Wong Brother. Now there was no time to speak one-to-one with anybody. My face crumpled. In five months' time, we had all changed. More hardship lay ahead, but who knew what it would be? I desperately wanted to see how we would all turn out, but that was impossible. I wanted to shout that we should be happy to be alive. All I did was thank the men for helping me and taking care of me. They did not know what to say either. We all looked awkward and gloomy. When Fung clapped me on the shoulder, I almost burst into tears. That was when I ran back onto the boat.

On the boat, Ba speaks loudly, as if he is a town official. I don't understand (as usual) but he tells the workers that there should have been newsmen and picture-takers at the site today, to record our deed. He says that we should be proud of ourselves, and that more Red Beards need to hear about our work so that in the future, Chinese people can live in Canada. But why would we live so far from home? Someone scoffs and calls Ba a madman.

The river swirls angrily through steep cliffs, and *Skuzzy* steers around the many rapids. On rocks jutting over the water, Nlaka'pamux people fish with long-handled nets. They clean the fish and let it dry on racks. I envy their freedom. I envy how they have friends and families close by.

I write now to look busy. At the cooking tent, no one will sit by me. No one is near my age like Wong Brother. Did we both go north, or take opposite routes?

September 23, near Salmon River

The iron road is blocked by the mountain's foot. Instead of tunnelling through it, the Red Beards will blast it away. Good! No tunnel means no rocks will drop from above and split open our heads. Already, the crew has pushed a cut deep into the rock.

My legs are sore. I am not used to going up and down, up and down all day long. We climb a zigzag of narrow wooden planks to escape the cut. Then we clamber up another slope to the top. We inch to the edge and tip the rubble into the river below. We are two crews of Chinese, but Red Beard drillers and blasters make all the noise. When they ignite a charge, they blow a whistle three times. It is barely enough time to get away because the cut goes so deep.

The first thing I asked Ba was how much money he had saved. He glared and called me insolent for failing to trust him. I desperately wanted to ask how much we owed, but my courage failed me. In Ba's tent, the only free sleeping spot was far from him. Later, I felt bad because our tent-mates chuckled at seeing how I was not near Ba. Am I really a bad son?

September 24

I trekked along the river, looking for a fishing spot, but rubble and cliffs blocked my way. I climbed back to the iron road path.

Several sites contained tents and tall machines. The smell of spicy meats frying in the Red Beard tents made me hungry. Some Chinese greeted me cheerfully; others looked half-asleep and did not speak a word. Some squatted at the river, washing clothes. I watched the Nlaka'pamux men fish. It takes a very keen eye to spear a fish swimming through water.

From high in the mountain, a crackling stream shot down. Over it, Red Beards were building a bridge. It looked like a long rattan cage for crickets. Closer up, I saw heavy logs, carefully fitted together. Red Beard men called out, but I didn't understand. They alarmed me, so I headed home.

Ba was at the river washing clothes. Ox Uncle laughed at him, "Why wash your own clothes? Get your son to do it!"

"Him? He has no talent for anything," Ba replied. "I'll do it myself."

I stomped away not knowing whether to curse him or to thank him.

That evening, men were shouting and cheering as they gambled in a tent. No doubt Ba was there. Poy Uncle will tell me about Ba's money, but I must find the right moment to ask.

September 26

What a pleasure to eat fresh meat. It was not beef or pork, but wild game that Cook had killed. What a good man! He took his long gun into the forest to hunt for us.

I forgot about Mid-Autumn. That was why Cook had made special food. Everyone stayed up to see the full moon. Some men toasted it with wine. Tofu Boy said the moon was bigger and brighter back home. To me it looked the same. The big difference was how cold the night was.

All the children on our street used to put candles into newly made lanterns for the festival. When they were lit, the dyed papers threw bright colours onto our faces, and the lantern parade twisted through the dark like a dragon. And what a feast we had. I pushed away those memories. I was no child now.

September 27

I almost fell into the cut. I was climbing but slipped. Someone had spat onto the plank. I swayed back and forth. I almost toppled but someone steadied my carrying-pole from behind. Last thing I needed was to hurt my leg. Later, I thanked the fellow, Tiger Face.

In camp no one ate with him. Several months ago he had quit the crew to go gold-mining. He had no luck and came back to work. Unhappily, he ended up with his old crew. They called him Traitor and Double Failure. In his view, Ba worked too hard. How could that be? I only hear Ba talk about gambling.

September 29

Ba told me to stay away from Tiger Face. "He's a loser," he said. I kept my mouth shut. Ba must stop telling me what to do. Besides, Tiger Face is closer to my age than anyone else here.

October 1

Ba and Poy Uncle spent the day in the gambling tent.

I trekked upriver and then followed a stream inland. Birds chirped in the dense trees and bushes. It was so peaceful that I thought no one had ever been here. Then, I saw Nlaka'pamux men, women and children, staring at me. I wanted to call out, but my throat dried up. I had walked into their house without being invited. I ran back to camp and slept all day.

Woo asked me to write a letter. Poy Uncle had told him about my handiwork. Woo's son had sent no letters, and Woo wanted to know about the recent harvest and if their roof had been re-tiled. I read my words back to him, to make sure he was happy.

I hope he will spread the word about my little business. If Ba tells me to stop, I will refuse.

October 3

The plank was slippery from rain and Little Snake toppled backwards into the cut. Now he cannot walk properly. Ever since last week I have been especially careful. But Bookman told me to hurry up.

Puppy complained about his rain cape leaking. Thunder God sneered about low-quality Western goods from the Company store. Then Puppy pointed out how Thunder God was wearing Western pants and boots. Thunder God exclaimed, "And look how they are ripped!"

What do you expect? I thought to myself. We work around sharp rocks!

These men complain all day long, like lazy house servants.

October 6

Ox Uncle and Tiger Face were near the rock face when the whistle sounded. They ran out of the cut and were almost safe when the blast went off. Rocks flew into the air and down to the river. A chunk of mountain hit Ox Uncle and knocked him to the ground. He has trouble raising his right arm.

Ba ran to Bookman and a huge argument erupted. Ba wanted Bookman to tell the Red Beards to blow the whistle earlier. Bookman claimed he had done so, but Crew Boss said that his men could not control the explosions. Ba pointed out they were in too much of a hurry.

Would Ba have made a fuss for someone else? Of course he would stand up for his gambling buddy Ox Uncle.

October 8

Ba showed me a letter from home. Right away it gave me hope. Ma told Ba to send me home! She complained about life with Ba's cousin. Stinky Uncle and Stinky Aunty's sons bullied Little Brother. They treated her and Little Brother like servants. Stinky Aunty would not call Ma to dinner. Ma feared Stinky Uncle's sons, and hid in her room all day. Grandfather got so angry that he went to live with his friend. He asked if we had earned enough money for a new business.

When I finished, Ba grabbed the letter but said nothing. I saw myself in Stinky Uncle's house, standing in front of Ma and Little Brother. "You want to speak to my mother or brother?" I would say. "You talk to me first."

But there is no money to send me home.

October 15

An entire week passed without worthy events, so I did not write. It rained today. I wish there was someone to go fishing with me. Does Cook ask permission from the Nlaka'pamux people before he goes hunting? Cook usually takes Helper with him so that they can carry the kill to camp. Maybe one day he will take me.

I was so bored that I even listened to the men argue politics. Little Snake predicts that China and Japan will go to war soon, and that China will lose. What? How can a Chinese person say that? The men growl at him and label him a traitor, but Little Snake tells us to look at the recent events in Korea.

Both China and Japan sent troops there after Koreans revolted against rulers who favoured Japan. Little Snake says China made a big mistake: its troops should have helped the Koreans fight the Japanese instead of helping the Japanese punish the Koreans. He claims China was afraid to do so because it knew that Japan's army and navy were stronger.

This caused Shrimp Boy to call Little Snake a double traitor for urging that China go into battle while knowing that China would lose! By this time, everyone in the tent was shouting. It made me think of all the differences between Grandfather, Ba and me, and how we have never settled them.

October 16

The floor of the cut has two inches of mud and water. As we took our baskets, Ba said, "Don't walk beneath the edge of the slope. Earth can slide down from above."

I went right under it. If you're scared, I thought, then you shouldn't work here.

"Rock Brain, you should listen to me!" yelled Ba. "If you get hurt, don't call me!"

I would rather bite my tongue off, I thought, than call you for help.

Everyone heard Ba call me Rock Brain. Now they all call me that. I hate Ba.

October 17

Ba was right. A huge blanket of mud, rocks, trees and bushes slid into the cut. We heard loud rumbling and the alarm was sounded. But no one knew where to run. Blind Eye and Saltwater Crisp got trapped under it. Luckily a huge tree got jammed above their heads, and deflected the rocks rolling down. I had been following them all morning, but I went to pee. That saved me from getting caught with them. Lucky me! Poy Uncle said he had seen worse, where landslides covered entire cuts and crushed the workers.

When Saltwater Crisp got pulled from the mud and rocks, the sole of his boot flapped loosely. It looked like a dog's jaw, opening and closing. The boot was two weeks new, he said, and should have held up better.

Poy Uncle told Bookman, "See, if we don't slow down the work, then Heaven will do it for us."

October 20

We were clearing the mudslide when we got called away. *Skuzzy* took us across the river, where a huge pile of lumber lay on the shore, half in the water.

We untangled the wood, dragged it to the road, and loaded it onto wagons. Earlier this morning, a too-strong current had consumed the boat's fuel, leaving it unable to reach its destination. To lighten the load, sailors had dumped the timber overboard.

"We were hired to build the iron road," complained Shrimp Boy. "The Red Beards should clean up their own mess."

October 21

Payday. I have worked one hundred and thirty-two days. I owe $13.60 for the ship passage. Ba and Poy Uncle have only $10 left to pay.

When Ba demanded to know why I still owed so much, I told him I had been sick for three weeks. He snorted and reminded me that I should drink only boiled water.

I vowed to never get sick again. Ba doesn't care about people getting sick, not when they get injured and killed so readily here. He is hard-hearted. All my life he has been like that. I guess he is trying to toughen me for a tough life ahead. But even stingy Old Foo, the merchant at home that no-one will work for, gives to beggars. Ba never gives to beggars. Grandfather did, and so did Ma.

After Ba strode away, I casually asked Poy Uncle if Ba was getting close to reclaiming our wages.

"Heen, you should have come two months ago!" he exclaimed. Ba went on a winning streak for over two weeks. He gambled in town, where the stakes were much higher, and won there too. Poy Uncle lost count but he was sure Ba had won enough to clear our debts! Then Ba's luck changed, for the worse. When Poy Uncle saw my stricken face, he grinned and recited a proverb to reassure me: *Not just one door, for good luck or for poor.*

Finally he added, "Your Ba's not worried, so why are you worried?"

Could he be right? Is there really nothing to worry about?

October 22

Men went to town to spend their earnings, but I wrote letters and earned money instead. Puppy urged his mother to cook healing foods for his wife, who had given birth to his second child. Tofu Boy asked his father to see if the neighbour would sell his land. Like me, these men were keen to go home. I found out that Bookman charges twice as much to write letters! I should get plenty of customers here.

The clerk at the Company store refused to serve Tiger Face due to his poor work record. The Company fears that Tiger Face will not stay long enough to pay his bills.

Ba gave me my first pair of gloves. I pulled them on and off a thousand times. I asked if I would be going home to take care of Ma and Little Brother.

"Ma can look after things," he declared. "And Little Brother needs to learn to fight for himself."

Ha! Ba hardly knows Little Brother. He is clever but not a fighter.

October 23

Two men did not return from town. On payday, they had cursed loudly at how little they had earned and how much they owed the Company. They joined the crew just before I arrived, but greatly disliked the food and the work.

October 24

Woo Uncle and a Red Beard died. They had drilled the rock and tapped in blasting powder. The explosion gave no warning. Two nearby Red Beards suffered deep cuts from flying rock. Bookman said we were lucky the men had carried in only a little bit of powder. If a full case of powder had been sitting there, more workers would be dead.

Bookman asked Ba to write a letter to Woo Uncle's family. Ba looked angry enough to bite, like a dog. He asked what caused the explosion.

Bookman did not know. Ba shouted, "You don't know? Or you don't *want* to know?"

Why is Ba so upset? He and Woo were not friends, from what I saw.

I almost blurted out that I had written a letter for Woo a few weeks ago. But I kept quiet because I did not want to be asked to write this next letter. I would not know what to say. I can only hope that the harvest Woo Uncle was asking about was a good one.

October 26

This morning, when our breath hit the cold air outside, it formed warm clouds. I wore my padded jacket. Ba had a Western jacket of heavy cloth. It was too small for him. Was it bought or was it won in a game? Had it been traded back and forth many times like a prized piece of jade?

Old Fire checked his almanac and announced First Frost.

"Chinese calendars are useless here!" Thunder God snorted. "This is Canada!"

At work, a plank broke under Old Fire, Shrimp Boy and Little Snake. They fell into the cut and got bruised, but went back to work later.

Tiger Face wore his three shirts and two pairs of pants, everything he owned. He still shivered from the cold. Sell-Ginger warned us about such weather. Will it kill us?

October 27

At Woo Uncle's grave, we had trouble poking incense into the cold ground. Thunder God said good thing we had buried Woo right away. Otherwise we would have struggled to dig through frozen soil. Every crew member came and bowed his head and paid solemn respects. This impressed me. In my other gang, not everyone could afford to attend the funeral and lose his wages.

Shrimp Boy gave Tiger Face another shirt. Now everyone is wearing everything.

October 29

We walked to town through the rain. I told the clerk to put Tiger Face's purchases on my account, but he called a helper. They checked the ledger and then they looked up, smirking.

"You're the big spender? Hah! You're being generous? Don't make me laugh! All your wages belong to someone else."

Tiger Face frowned. Gleefully, the clerks pointed us out to other customers: "Look, this one barely worked. And the other one earns money that doesn't belong to him! Can there be sillier customers? Which of these fools is more stupid, do you think?"

Tiger Face clenched his fist, wanting to take a swing at them. Luckily, Poy Uncle put everything on his account.

November 1

A Red Beard was drilling when a sharp chip flew into his eye. He clapped his hand over it, which drove the splinter in farther. He screamed and staggered about. The steam drills are powerful and their damage goes deep. They are hissing snakes. The Red Beards' machines do the work of fifty men, but those hoses and sharp tips can betray the ones who built them.

The past days warmed up like summer but rain came along. Tiger Face complains he purchased too much warm clothing.

November 5

It snowed last night. The trees and mountains have the same shapes as before but now they are a different colour. All looks peaceful, which is deceiving. Our explosions are dark clouds of dust. Our boots turn the snow black.

Men discuss plans for the winter. Ba said

nothing. Will we go home to China? Or head south to town?

Poy Uncle will stay here. At first I thought I misheard. The cooking tent is left behind so Poy Uncle will move there. Firewood and coal from the Company store will keep him warm. He will buy food and cook his own. Others are pooling funds to join him. "Cheaper than sailing to China," he brags, "and cheaper than going to town. Landlords raise their rents because workers have nowhere to go."

Later, Ba told me to help Poy Uncle fix the cooking tent and fetch supplies. Ba has put money into the pool for me. I will stay here while he goes south. He asked me if I was scared.

"No," I lied. "What's there to fear here?" Then I blurted, "Don't you think I should go home? Ma and Little Brother need protection."

Ba retorted, "We need every penny for Grandfather."

"Our wages are gone," I snapped, "and you'll gamble all winter."

"It's the only way to get the money we need," Ba insisted.

I took a deep breath and demanded that he hand over the money whenever he won. I would keep it safe from being lost in another game. Ba looked at me if I had gone crazy.

"You win money and then you lose it," I cried out. "I just want Grandfather to get back his store!"

"Don't you think I want the same thing?" snapped Ba.

"You won enough money!" I pointed out. "Poy Uncle told me!"

"Poy Uncle doesn't know a thing! He can't count!"

November 6

After terrible cold, it is warm again. Our padded jackets and extra blankets eat up too much space in the tent.

November 8

The warning whistle sent us running. After the blast came the all-clear signal. The whistle kept going.

We had broken through the foot of the mountain, we had cut our way out of the cut! Blind Eye and I climbed to look through the breach. We seemed high up. I saw thick forests, more rocks and more mountains, and a stream running by. I had seen it before, while looking for a fishing spot.

We kept working. Why lose half a day's wages? The Red Beards crossed the stream to the next mountain. Our work sped up as we dumped our baskets over the breach instead of climbing to the river's edge.

November 9

No Red Beards worked today. National holiday, Bookman said, to thank God for a rich harvest. Saltwater Crisp called out, "Do we get a day to thank Queen of Heaven for bringing us here safely?"

"Are you still praying?" Tofu Boy laughed. "No god protects us! Home is too far away."

In the middle of the day, Nlaka'pamux men strode through the breach. They watched us work, shaking their heads as if they felt sorry for us. Bookman fetched Crew Boss, who shouted at the visitors.

Some wore Western clothes and boots, but others had animal-skin hats and long shirts sewn with beads and fringes. The tallest man was wrapped in a coat that fell to his knees. Shiny animal fur showed on the collar and inside, while fringes thick as strings of brown-wrapped firecracker dangled from the sleeves. They carried heavy poles. Were these weapons? They spoke forcefully. Crew Boss and Bookman went away with them.

Later, Bookman told us to be careful at the stream. Debris was blocking it. The Nlaka'pamux people said fish could not get upstream to give birth. Crew Boss assured them the iron road would run on a bridge over the stream. They wanted the debris cleared and the stream restored, so we moved the rubble a second time.

November 10

A horrible death marred our start at the next mountain. After the warning whistle, we scattered to safety. But the explosion came far too soon. Rocks hurtled out and hit several men. Worst of all, a sharp flat rock spun through the air and cut off Puppy's head. I did not think I could write this, but I have.

At first no one noticed. Then I heard people retching and wailing. Ba seized a pole and ran after Crew Boss. I grabbed a rock and followed. Crew Boss turned and fled. Stupidly, he ran to the river, where rocks blocked his path. He couldn't get back up because our crew had rallied behind Ba. Everyone shouted and cursed. Blind Eye wailed like an old woman at a funeral. Crew Boss ran into the water. We hurled rocks at him. Ba and I chased him, but the water was icy. Let him soak in the water, we thought, so we stood and watched him. Cook came running with his rifle, and fired into the air. Crew Boss dared not come to shore. Finally, Red Beards rowed out a boat, picked him up, and took him across the river.

November 12

I went with Poy Uncle and Thunder God to get winter supplies: mostly firewood. I had hoped a passing boat might help us. No such luck. At the store, a letter had arrived for Puppy. We took it back to camp, but no one opened it. Bookman told me to write to Puppy's family. There is no pay for such letters.

November 16

I have not written to Puppy's family. I wanted to ask Ba what he wrote in his letter to Woo Uncle's family, but then Ba would call me Rock Brain again.

I doubt there is anything I can do that would make Ba respect me. I saw Poy Uncle shake his head and say to Ba, "You still think we all should die here? You still think Red Beards respect us for dying on the job?"

Ba looked down without speaking. These days, he looks sadder than when I first joined this crew.

November 19

Thunder God, Old Fire, Blind Eye and I went to town and brought back sacks of coal for winter. To keep them dry, we covered them with sheets of heavy canvas. We made the tent stronger by tying more ropes from the corners of the tent to pegs pounded into the ground. Now everyone must be careful not to trip over them. We had to work fast, because the sky gets dark earlier and earlier each day.

Rain has fallen during each of the five past weeks. Wet clothes will not dry, so we all stink. I wrote a letter to Puppy's family. It made me sick.

November 21

Payday. Ba claimed Puppy owed him money but Bookman said Puppy still owed money to the Company.

I was surprised not to lose pay for the time used for the deaths of Woo Uncle and Puppy. I asked Bookman if this rule held for all workers under the Company's rule. He shook his head and said, "I told Crew Boss the ghosts of the dead Chinese will haunt him if he is not generous."

November 22

Red Beards and Chinese are heading south. Some trek on the iron road path, others ride boats on the river. It was colder upriver, Bookman said. But this site was warmer, so we would work to the next payday. "When it gets cold," he added, "Cook makes hot tea at the cut."

Ten men left. At departure, Little Snake urged Ba to go south with them to avoid freezing to death. When Ba said he had to stay and look after me, Little Snake told him to bring me south too, because I would never survive winter up here.

Oh yes I will, I thought. I'll show Ba that I'm up to any task.

November 25

Our two crews work under one boss now.

My carrying-pole snapped and spilled everything. Poy Uncle said that when moisture freezes inside the wood, the ice breaks the bamboo fibres. Now everyone tests their carrying-poles before work.

November 26

Rain and cold caused more people to head south. Tiger Face decided to stay, so that makes seven men. Good thing the cooking tent is bigger than our tents. We looked for trees and branches to put on the floor to lift our beds off the cold ground. But during the night, the tree trunks will roll away, and so your neighbour curses you, or you wake up with a sore back next morning.

November 27

Mid-morning, Tiger Face and I went to get tea. Cook said, "No more."

He pointed to his fire, where a big pot perched on blackened rocks. The fire was out.

"Crew Boss doused it," Cook said.

Tiger Face and I squatted and thrust our fingers under the pot. The rocks were still hot so we pressed their warmth to our necks and cheeks. Saltwater Crisp and Ox Uncle came by. We passed them the hot rocks. Turning around, I saw our entire crew squatting there, waiting for the hot rocks. It was a relief to get warm, even for a second.

Crew Boss and Bookman ran up.

"Get back to work!" shouted Bookman.

"You said we would have hot tea," Tofu Boy reminded him. Ox Uncle and others echoed him: "We want hot tea!"

We stayed firm and shouted, "No tea, no work! No tea, no work!"

Crew Boss cursed Bookman, who swore back. Finally, Crew Boss marched off and Bookman went to Cook. "Start the fire!" he said, hiding a smile. "Make the tea as hot as you can."

November 29

The Chinese contractor rode a sleek brown horse. A long gun was slung across his back; a pistol hung at his belt. He wore Western clothes and smoked a cigar, even in the rain. He looked younger than Ba but not as strong.

"Hot tea?" he shouted. "Is that what your sit-down strike was for? Hot tea? Who started the strike?"

It was no strike, I told myself. Crew Boss saw something that wasn't here. Luckily, nobody helped the bosses. Cook didn't know who was responsible because he had left after Crew Boss doused the fire. When he came back, the workers had already gathered. As for Bookman, he said he didn't arrive until Crew Boss yelled. So he didn't see the start either.

"This must not happen," Contractor shouted. "The Chinese company makes rules for food and drink. Crew Boss works for the Red Beard firm. He cannot tell you what to drink or eat. But if he thinks the work is slowing, then he will act. Make sure you know everything before doing stupid things."

There was nothing stupid about what we did! It was bitterly cold.

Ba did not say anything, but I wonder if he knows that Tiger Face and I were the ones who started this. Even if he does, he won't give me credit for a good deed. But I deserve it!

November 30

The Red Beards did not work. They are Americans. It is their day to thank God for the harvest. I thought they and the Canadians worshipped one God.

We unpacked the winter food and found a disaster. Little insects crawled among the dried fruits and the dried tofu sticks. The jars of pickled vegetables were mouldy. It will be extra work to carry everything back for an exchange.

December 3

At the store, Poy Uncle cursed the clerks. They refused to exchange the shoddy goods. They blamed us, accusing us of not storing the foods properly. Poy Uncle stomped out and left the food behind. I made a list of the goods. He vowed to get satisfaction.

December 5

We heard the warning whistle and scrambled to get out. But the blast came too soon and knocked Tiger Face to the ground. Now his face is cut up, and his mouth is full of broken teeth and blood. He lies in his tent groaning in pain. We piled on many blankets to keep him warm in the cold.

Both Ba and Poy Uncle shouted at Bookman to tell the blasters to blow their warning whistle earlier. There have been many new Red Beard workers because so many have headed south.

December 7

Poy Uncle is gone.

We heard the warning whistle and ran for cover. Then came a loud bang, followed by another and then another. The rumble of falling rocks and trees came after. They crashed into the stream. We heard the all-clear whistle and went back to work.

Poy Uncle had helped a Red Beard carry the steam drill to the rock face. Then another bang sent a shower of gravel hissing through the air. At the rock face, Poy Uncle and the Red Beard were dead. Flying rocks had killed them. One of the powder charges had been late in exploding.

"I told men not to rush back in," Bookman moaned. "They should wait longer."

Tiger Face said, "I think the mountain gods are angry."

I thought for sure Ba would scream and shout at Bookman, but he did no such thing. He hugged himself tightly, and scrunched his face up tight, as if he wanted to cry. All the men looked anxiously at Ba. They too expected him to unleash a storm of anger at Bookman and Crew Boss. But he didn't.

I worry about Ba. Poy Uncle was his best friend. They worked together for many years. If only there was something comforting that I could do or say.

December 8

As we dug a grave for Poy Uncle, snow started falling. The large flakes were big enough to catch on a finger, to hold for a half a second. Tears streamed down my cheek. I had known Poy Uncle for as long as I had lived. Ba's rigid face showed no feelings.

Heading back to work, Ba walked stiffly beside me. I was about to hurry on ahead when he spoke: "Son, if I should die, then you must leave for home right away. Our family can afford to give only one life to the iron road."

My ears perked up like a rabbit's. I am ashamed to admit that even at such a sad time, I thought about myself first. I wanted to say "What?" and have Ba repeat himself. I wanted to hear him call me "son" again.

"What if I should die first?" I replied slowly. "Would you go home right away?"

I was surprised when Ba did not say yes. Would he really stay here? Earlier, Tiger Face had said Ba took his work too seriously. What was Ba thinking?

December 10

At Poy Uncle's grave, Ba whispered, "Old Friend, I will do one more thing for you."

By chance, a boat was ferrying workers to town. We boarded and told everyone about Poy Uncle. In town, we marched to the store. Ba took Poy Uncle's list inside. When he came out, someone slammed the door.

"They won't make good on the shoddy food," he shouted. "What should we do?"

The men surrounded the building and thumped its walls with rocks. The door flew open. Contractor pointed his gun at the sky and fired. Everyone stopped.

"Get away from the store!" he shouted.

No one moved. He pointed his gun at Ba. "I will kill him!"

Nothing happened.

"Move back!" he cried. "Or I open fire!"

Two Red Beards dashed up. They pointed guns at Contractor and screamed in English. Contractor lowered his weapon.

"Police officials want you to disband," he yelled. "They must have peace and order here."

We hurled curses at him.

"The officials order you to leave!" he shouted. "What do you want?"

"Give us satisfaction," Ba said.

Contractor shook his head. Men pounded the store walls. The Red Beards shouted at Contractor. Finally, he turned to Ba and growled, "This time I'll give you what you want. But only for the sake of peace."

Red Beards led Ba and Contractor away. I followed them but was stopped at a building. Contractor came out and snarled, "Your leader will go to jail. You better run before the police arrest all of you for damaging the store."

December 11

All day long, I kept looking around, expecting to see Ba come back to work. It was hard to believe that Ba had been arrested. He was just trying to get a refund on shoddy goods. Customers who returned rice to our store always got satisfaction.

Bookman cursed Ba for making trouble. Ba would go before a judge, he said, and would go to jail if found guilty. The good news was that the jailers will feed Ba, for I cannot take food to him every day. Only nine days of work remain, but that is $9 that we will not earn. Ba acted because of Poy Uncle's death, so I hope staying in jail makes him less sad. Still, it must be hard to be alone.

Today was the coldest day ever, worsened by thick clouds that darkened the afternoon well before it was time to stop work. I never imagined that temperatures could go so low. Luckily, Ma had believed such talk, and forced me to bring warm clothing.

December 13

It snowed last night. At work, something hit my neck. I reached back. It felt cold and wet. I turned around and something hit my cheek. It stung and I howled with pain.

The Red Beards were throwing snow! They packed handfuls of snow into lumps that became heavy enough to hurl. When Old Fire, Tofu Boy and I figured out their stunt, we fought back with our own snow lumps. When Bookman came running, I aimed one straight at him. Then everyone joined in to throw snow lumps at Bookman. We all laughed loudly. Bookman looked as if he had just walked through a snowstorm!

December 15

I hardly slept last night. I was cold, even with Ba's blankets atop mine, even with my gloves on. If Ma learns Ba might go to prison, she will worry. If Stinky Uncle and Stinky Aunty find out, they will treat her and Little Brother like criminals. Grandfather will frown. It brings shame to the family name. Worst of all, if Ba is in prison, he won't be able to gamble and win the money we need.

December 17

The walk to town took longer due to the snow. The sun provided no warmth. The store clerks were rude, so I left without asking about Ba.

I had reached the outskirts of town when I kicked myself. Rock Brain! I turned around and went to the laundry. Men loitered there, puffing on water pipes, sipping tea and complaining about the weather. The owner worked at the bench, by irons heating on the pot-bellied stove. Everyone called him Hot Water Wing.

I took a breath and spoke. "Uncle, here, if the police arrest you, how long do you wait for the trial?"

Right away, the men stopped talking and started listening.

"Why ask?" snapped Hot Water Wing. "You didn't get arrested."

"My father was," I replied. "A few days ago, when there was trouble at the Company store."

Ah! Suddenly all the men were talking. My father would eat no rice in jail, only potatoes. The jailers emptied the bucket just once a week. Good thing the officials were honest. Too bad the punishment was severe. Two men had been arrested for making trouble at the Company store last year. One man was sentenced to five years in prison; the other was sent away for eighteen months. Their terms were served down the river, at Second City, where I had spent a night on the boat.

I walked home slowly. If Ba went to prison for five years, the iron road might be finished by the time he was set free. Who would remember him?

December 18

Crew Boss and Bookman shouted at the Red Beards and at us. The work has slowed. The packed snow is slippery. When we fall, it is painful. We get wet and then the cold stays with us all day. My behind still feels numb from my tumble. Thunder God had the worst fall. He tripped and landed on his knee. He couldn't walk for the rest of the day.

December 20

A half-hearted cheer sounded at the end of day. We thought accounts would get settled tomorrow, but Bookman wanted to leave right away in the morning. He lit candles in the cooking tent and we all filed in.

Winter is expensive here! I had to buy shirt, gloves, warm socks, sweater, scarf and underwear. I had to pay the school tax to the government here. I hear that last year the Chinese workers protested this tax, but then armed police officers marched into the camps to get payment. I have $57.45 to my name while Ba has $63.65 to his. The difference is not big, yet he treats me like a child. I wish Ba had told me how much money he had lost. Are there enough funds for me to go home? Now he is in jail and everything is up to me. The police will have taken the money he had in his pockets. I am sure he told nobody at home about our money trouble, so if things get worse, it will be me who delivers the bad news. As far as I can see, he is not worried about the debt. He wins and he loses in the games, but no one can tell me if he saved any money.

I wish I had never come to Canada.

December 21

I was not leaving camp so I slept until almost mid-day! What better way was there to enjoy my new freedom?

Outside, only two tents were standing; the campsite looked bleak and pitiful. Trees crept closer, shadows loomed darker, and the cooking tent shrank. All was deathly quiet. A sharp wind whistled through and made me shiver. Suddenly I needed to hear explosions, shrill whistles and heavy drilling.

Tiger Face helped carry my bed logs to the tent. We pounded stakes into the ground to stop them from rolling. Old Fire bragged about his second winter here and scoffed, "A little cold and you cannot sleep on the ground?"

The men laughed while saying goodbye.

"If you have no food, eat Rock Brain." Ox Uncle chuckled. "Boys have tender flesh!"

Shrimp Boy and Helper were the lucky ones. They will sail for China!

"Do not be lazy," Cook said to me. "Walk to town whenever you can. Otherwise you will go crazy, living with these fools."

In the tent, we will take turns cooking, cleaning and getting supplies. Every fifteen days, a new person begins. Old Fire starts. Poy Uncle had bought the basic groceries. The budget for each term is set. Anyone who overspends will pay the difference from his own pocket. Any extra money, however, gets carried over to the next term. Because I have a notebook, they told me to keep the accounts. Why should I? This is rest time! I am sick of being ordered around. If I could go back to China too, that would be best.

December 22

Old Fire has no recent details about Yale, so I must go to town before I can set out to see Ba. But Blind Eye and Saltwater Crisp begged Tiger Face and I to help find and chop down bed logs.

I had little to do today. In the eight months of work this year, thirteen workers around me were killed while on the job. Ba and I are lucky to be alive. And, at least thirty-one accidents happened. I wonder if Ma will ever see me again. And if she does, will I still possess all my body parts? Will she recognize my face?

December 23

The cooler it is, the longer the trek to town feels. Ba's crew should be closer to town. Who needs this extra walking? Why do other people get all the luck? I must walk past three camps to reach town. No matter how fast I walk, I do not get warm.

At the wash house, customers leave piles of dirty clothes everywhere. Chinese workers bang through the door and shout if anyone had seen so-and-so in town. At most camps, Chinese are staying the winter. While the weather is nice, people come to town. Everyone likes the laundry. It uses hot water for washing, and the building is warm enough to dry clothes. Hot Water Wing has a big woodshed.

Sadly I did not see any familiar faces. The owner said walking to Yale would take two days. "Ride the train, if it is running," he said. "Cold weather might slow it down. The train can only take you part of the way. Not all the tunnels are open yet."

I did not mention I had no money for the train. I planned to beg for food along the way, at Chinese camps. I would also be stealing heat from their fires.

At the wash house, men were arguing. Chinese troops had marched into Vietnam to help repel European invaders. This time the enemy was a country called France. Some men felt the Chinese army should stay home and protect China. Others argued that if Vietnam fell, then the West would surround China and take our homeland too. I felt grown-up, following the debate. Too bad I had no views to offer.

December 24

I got up to trek to Yale, but Old Fire cried out, "Not today! It's First of Winter!"

Indeed, there was fresh snow, but it did not last the day. Old Fire planned to make soup and to knead rice-flour dough for winter balls. My mouth watered and so I decided to wait a day.

December 25

Instead of being halfway to Yale, I am crouched by the little stove in our tent, writing by the light of the flames. In the middle of the night, my stomach started hurting. I jumped into my boots and ran to the latrine. To my surprise, Thunder God was there, groaning. After he left, Blind Eye hurried up, clutching his stomach and his mouth. Outside the tent, Saltwater Crisp was bent over, vomiting.

Now no one wants to eat Old Fire's food. Tiger Face joked that Old Fire was trying to poison us so that he would not have to cook at all!

I wonder if I can live through this winter.

December 27

Today I felt stronger and set out for Yale. The men wished me a safe trip and predicted that I would get better food along the way. Unfortunately, the journey did not work out. It started snowing again. Each step I took left a hole in the deep snow.

Then I met a very strange man. At the second camp, someone called and ran out in long loping steps. It was an old man with a white beard, wrapped in a long, ragged coat. He warned me that people had seen animal tracks near the trail. It might be a cougar. "You are too young to be alone!" he said. "Turn around and go home!"

I ignored him but he grabbed my arm. I tried to shake him off but he had a strong grip. I was furious. How dare he stop me?

He realized I was determined to go, so he softened his tone and asked, "Don't you want to work next season?"

Hah! That was the last thing I wanted, and I let him hear me clearly.

He chuckled and said that if I could see into the future, then I would change my mind. When I pointed out how impossible that was, he said *he* could tell the future. So I asked him what he saw for me. He put his hand on my forehead and shut his eyes.

"You, you will soon see your mother, brother and grandfather," he said. "They will be overjoyed to receive you. But you do not bring enough for them, and you will want to come back here. But by then it will be too late."

How did he know I had a brother?

Then he told me not to go to Yale. He told me to stay the winter and build the iron road.

Enough! I stomped back to the trail. Ma and Grandfather in China needed me!

But by now, the snow was falling heavily. It reduced the light. I couldn't see the path. The snow came to my knees at each step. I slowed down.

Then my toes got wet and cold as water seeped into my boot. I would have kept on going if my stomach had not started to feel strange again. To be sick and cold and alone was too much to bear and I finally turned around.

The trip seemed to take forever. When I got home, the men in the tent scoffed at news of the cougar, as if they didn't believe me. Saltwater Crisp accused me of fearing the cold. I got tired of arguing. They can believe whatever they want. If they get eaten by a cougar, it won't be my fault.

December 28

When I fell asleep last night, two insights came to me.

Going to Yale is useless. Ba already paid for my stay in this tent. He will never change his mind and let me go to China.

Secondly, that man on the trail was no fortune-teller. All he said were a few things that applied to every person working here. I am sure he is a madman.

December 30

Choy, a same-village friend of Thunder God, came for a visit. He brought a jug of rice wine and drank with Thunder God. They chatted and laughed and ate peanuts that Poy Uncle had bought. Choy warned us to be careful in town, because gangs of Red Beards hurled hard-packed snow lumps at the Chinese.

After Choy left, Saltwater Crisp asked Thunder God to replace the bag of peanuts. Thunder God refused. He said everyone should feel free to welcome visitors. They brought news, gossip and jokes for everyone. Saltwater Crisp argued that meant strangers could stay here for free all winter. Thunder God called that an exaggeration.

Old Fire sided with Saltwater Crisp. When Thunder God asked for my view, I shrugged. I agreed with Thunder God because I would have asked for food in camps on the way to Yale. But Old Fire was the expert who had spent the previous winter here.

January 1, 1883

We have other unwelcome visitors. A mouse. Or mice. Yesterday Old Fire showed us the shreds of paper the rodents had gnawed to get at the bean sticks. We worried most about the rice, which Old Fire decided to hang from the roof. I was glad to have logs underneath me. Who wants mice running along his legs?

Old Fire walked to town for tin containers to

hold the food. But the Company store was closed for New Year's Day. Old Fire came back red with anger and soaking wet from the rain.

"That store should be open today," he declared. "Chinese people do not follow the Western calendar. The clerks are lazy, wanting to sleep the day away."

January 3

This morning, Old Fire started coughing. By day's end, Tiger Face had a tickle in his throat. Now I am coughing too, and my ribs are hurting.

All of us are weak and sick. Thunder God tripped over a root and landed on his bad knee. It turned black and purple, puffy and tender. He cannot put any weight on it. He must lie still, which is difficult for him. Good thing it is winter, otherwise he would lose pay. Thunder God curses his own stupidity for falling. If he were younger, he moans, his knee would heal quickly.

January 5

Old Fire's term ended yesterday and my turn started. I announced I knew nothing about kitchens or cooking. Blind Eye said no-one here did; we were all sinking in the same boat.

"No spitting or coughing into the rice pot," advised Thunder God, grinning.

Old Fire had overspent on rice flour and soup ingredients for First of Winter. Cheerfully he gave me money to replace what he had used up, and said, "My treat." Too bad I cannot be as generous.

January 7

Nobody left the tent yesterday or today. It is too cold. Snow falls so thickly you cannot see in front of you. Being stuck in a tent is painful. There is no silence because someone is always coughing. Tiger Face and I played chess, but he won all three matches. I tried to be a good loser but tired of the game. We shared a dim lantern with Old Fire, Salt-water Crisp and Blind Eye, who were playing with paper dominoes. Their shouting kept Thunder God from falling asleep, and he muttered angrily.

January 9

The men complained that I failed to wake up early enough to boil water and make tea for them. I told them to sleep in, to enjoy their rest. It had snowed and stayed cool, so all I need to do is step outside and fill my pails with snow to melt. It saves me from going up the mountain for running water or ice. That would wreck my boots even more.

When I started the fire, the room filled with smoke. People choked and sputtered and sounded sicker than ever. I feared I was causing everyone to die! Old Fire advised checking the chimney; snow might have blocked it. He also told me to scrape out the ashes from under the stove.

I offered to save firewood and money by not washing the bowls after meals. The men called me a lazy worm. "Do what Cook did," they commanded.

I cannot wait for my term to end. Ten more days to go.

January 13

Blind Eye and Thunder God scolded me when the soy sauce and salt ran out. I had no choice but to go to town. Passing the second camp, I thought about the cougar scare, but that was two weeks ago.

The trail had been worn into slippery ice by travellers, so it was safer to walk on fresh snow. The river rushed by, which led me to think it wasn't cold at all.

After buying salt and soy sauce, I stopped at Hot Water Wing's, looking for familiar faces. No luck. I lingered a while for the warmth. I should have left sooner, because when I finally went outside, it felt much cooler.

I headed out of town. Suddenly Red Beard men and boys surrounded me. I ran but they blocked my way. They danced around me, hooting and yelling. They brandished snow lumps. At a shouted signal, they hurled them at me. The jug of soy sauce flew from my hands. I covered my face with my hands, but Red Beards darted in and grabbed my gloves. Snow stung my cheeks and my eyes. As Red Beards stooped to scoop more snow, I ran from the circle. Hard lumps of snow thudded onto my back. I slipped several times but kept running until their shouts faded. Then I was all out of breath and had to slow down. Afterwards I couldn't get my feet to go faster, no matter how hard I pulled air into my lungs. I thought I might never get home.

By the time I reached camp, I could not feel my toes or my fingertips. I heated water on the stove. My skin had not hardened into ice although it was pale and white.

"Use warm water," advised Blind Eye. "If the water is too hot, it will burn you. Your skin is weak."

"What are you? Stupid?" sneered Saltwater Crisp. "Do you know how cold it is? Where are your gloves?"

"Be careful," warned Thunder God, "otherwise a doctor will saw off your legs."

Old Fire nodded solemnly. "If blood freezes in the veins, no-one can save you."

I claimed to have slipped and dropped the jug of soy sauce. The men shook their heads. I did not mention being pummelled by snow lumps. Tiger Face slowly added hot water to the basin, to make the water warmer.

January 15

Fate is cruel. If the salt or soy sauce had lasted two days longer, then I would be all right. No humiliation, no frostbite, no lecturing from the men.

The air is warm and soft, and it rained last night. Now the men track mud into the tent. The frozen ground oozes water. The men tell me to keep the floor dry. Otherwise, they say, we will all get sick.

I do not want to go to town. Not until all the snow is gone.

January 18

The disaster I was dreading happened today. I burned the rice. Ma always got upset about it being wasteful, stupid and bad luck. Here, I watched the rice pot carefully every time. Today I went to fetch firewood and, while outside, chopped a few sticks of kindling. Then I smelled burning rice. So did Old Fire and Blind Eye, who cursed my carelessness. I shouted them down.

They were shocked at my raised voice, especially when I was in the wrong. I offered to cook another pot and pay for the burnt rice from my own pocket. But the men backed off and did not speak to me all night. Fine by me!

January 19

Tiger Face came back from town with a letter from Ma. Uncle Stinky caught Little Brother stealing coins from his vest. Little Brother ran away and it took two days for Ma to find him and bring him home. She was forced to call Grandfather to lecture Little Brother and make him promise not to run away again. Then, Aunty Stinky snubbed Ma when they went to the temple for Mid-Autumn. She let her own sister go and present offerings before Ma's turn. Neighbours mentioned they had seen Grandfather gambling. Ma begged Ba or me to return. She asked if we had received her earlier letter, because she had not seen a reply.

I wanted to drop the letter into the stove. Instead I will forward it to Yale, and hope someone at the store will take it to Ba in the jail. I thought to tell Ma about the jail, but that will deepen her woes. Yet if Ba gets a long sentence, then later Ma will accuse me of hiding things from her.

Thank heaven for the end of my term! I plan

to sleep for days. Good luck to Tiger Face, who is next. Maybe he can do a better job than me.

January 28

The men are worrying about me. They think I am sick and weakening. I got tired of their concern, so I went and sat by the stove with my notebook. I had not written in a week. During those days, I slept and slept, while the men pestered me. Tiger Face asked me to play chess, but I shook my head. Thunder God proposed a poetry contest, but I pulled my blanket over my head. Old Fire and Saltwater Crisp offered to teach me how to play Heavenly Nines, but I said no. Ma's letter is still tucked in my notebook. Tiger Face could have taken it to town yesterday but I refused to move.

The men said it warmed up outside, so they had all gone visiting, either in town or at other camps.

Blind Eye went to visit a friend at Camp 27. By dark, he had not returned. Old Fire took a lantern outside, in case Blind Eye was lost nearby. Then he put on his coat. He wanted to walk up the trail to the other camp. The tent-mates advised against going because there was no saying where he might be.

"Maybe he stayed overnight with his friend," said Tiger Face.

"What if he got lost in the forest?" asked Old Fire. "How would you find him?

"He could have gone farther up the line," said Saltwater Crisp.

"What do you think, Rock Brain?" Old Fire called out.

I almost cried out, "I don't know! I'm just a boy!"

I was relieved when Old Fire stayed inside. We were all thinking of a story told in town. A worker walking to his home camp never arrived. Had he fallen into the river? Did a wild animal pounce on him? Had he been murdered for that night's gambling money?

Hours later Blind Eye stumbled in. I don't know how he found his way home. And I don't care.

January 31

Thunder God asked if I was dreaming about girls, if that was why I slept so much. I claimed to have no dreams. In truth, I did dream, but had no memory of them.

Tiger Face made a soup with healthful herbs. I am sure he used his own money to buy the ingredients. If he did it for me, he certainly did not let on.

Blind Eye asked me if I had any brothers or sisters. When I mentioned Little Brother, he asked if I missed him.

"Of course not!" I snapped. "I was glad to escape from that little pest."

Deep down, I worried about him.

February 2

Thunder God slipped on ice and fell backwards. When he tried to get up, he fell forward onto his bad knee. The pain makes him worry about work. The knee never healed from the first injury; the pain has never left. No-one knows what to do. Tiger Face took an axe into the forest to look for a tree branch that can work as a crutch. I should have gone with him but I was lazy.

Thick fog surrounded our site today. Sometimes it lifts by midday; other times it stays and stays.

February 3

Tiger Face went to town and had his forehead and straggly beard shaved. He looks handsome, and the men teased him.

"Too bad there's no mirror for you to see yourself," said Blind Eye.

"Too bad there are no pretty girls to smile at you," said Old Fire.

"You waste money!" cried Thunder God. "Men don't care how you look."

Some clever fellow curtained off some space in the wash house, and is doing a brisk business as a barber.

Tiger Face brought me some sweets. I advised him to save his money. He also brought news that six Chinese had died at Camp 14 from an illness. The tent was quiet after that. Saltwater Crisp said he knew people at that camp.

Next week is New Year. Tiger Face is offering to wash people's clothes for a small fee. He is clever. I wish I had thought of that. He can only wash one person's clothes each day, because there is no room in the tent for drying.

February 6

Blind Eye started his term two days ago. Today, he and Old Fire took each person's blankets outside, flung them open and shook them out with snapping sounds. Then they used tree branches to sweep away the grit and pebbles on the floor. They even tied open the door-flap, to let fresh air into the tent even though it was freezing.

"This isn't a home!" shouted Thunder God, angry at being disturbed. "You don't have to clean it up for the New Year. This isn't China!"

Blind Eye heated extra hot water for everyone to do a towel bath.

"Too cold outside," I mumbled. "I'm not taking off my clothes."

"You smell worse than the outhouse," he said. "Let me wash your clothes. You need a clean start for the New Year."

I smiled, in spite of my foul mood. Ma used to say "clean start" at this time of the year too.

February 8

Today was the big day. I forced myself to leave my bed and shout, "Happy New Year!" Old Fire exploded firecrackers just outside the tent. The smell of gunpowder reminded me of home: the eight-sided box loaded with sweets, crispy round dumplings, red scrolls bearing good wishes for the next year. I yearned for Ma and Grandfather and the red packets of good luck money.

Blind Eye surprised us with sweet red-bean soup. Sugar was expensive, so he had put in extra money. All the men showed good manners today: no cursing, no arguments, and no complaints.

Thunder God's friend Choy came with New Year greetings. He brought candied walnuts and a big jug of wine that he shared with everyone. He and Thunder God plan to pool their earnings and buy more farmland. They are eyeing a fertile site, located right beside the river. They asked the others what they planned for the future. Old Fire wanted to hire good tutors for his sons, and help them advance in the imperial exams. Blind Eye planned to invest his money in a business. I hadn't thought about my plans in a long time.

February 10

Very cold, but nothing stopped my tent-mates from going to town or visiting friends. I stayed behind with Thunder God. I did not want to walk all the way to town and find no friends there. The men see me as a boy and prefer to talk to their old buddies.

Thunder God was grateful for my company, and praised me for being a good boy. He also said kind things about Ba.

Tiger Face reported Chinese merchants in Yale have set up a hospital for Chinese workers. But he did not know if it had the same rules as the Red Beard's hospital, which accepted only workers who had been injured while working on the railway. If a worker just fell sick, the hospital would not take him. Thunder God wondered if he should go to Yale. But if he cannot walk properly, how can he get there?

February 13

It is too dark in the tent to see, and it is too cold to stay outside, so it was only at the latrine that

Old Fire saw blood on Saltwater Crisp's lips. Old Fire peered closer and saw blood oozing from the teeth. He noticed Saltwater Crisp's hands looked bruised, and asked what else was wrong. Nosebleeds. Losing two teeth. Queasy stomach.

Old Fire put on his coat, to go to town for herbs, but I offered to go. I had not been there in a month. I refused to be afraid anymore. I borrowed Old Fire's gloves and wrapped a shirt around my face, leaving a hole for my nose. This time, I did not get frostbite or attacked by snow-lump throwers. My only problem was how the sun, shining brightly on the snow, hurt my eyes.

Blind Eye made soup with the dried berries I brought back, and Old Fire told everyone to drink some. It tasted sour but not bitter like most herbal soups. Most of it went to Saltwater Crisp. I was surprised to learn that the same berries were used to make candies. Too bad the Company store didn't have any.

February 15

Tiger Face gave me a letter that was addressed to Poy Uncle. He had it last week, but refused to spoil New Year's week. I was determined not to get sad again and did not open it.

February 18

Blind Eye needed more berries, so I went to town again. The snow and ice were melting but it was foggy. At the Company store and the laundry, everyone was celebrating. People were too excited to talk to me. Two Chinese got arrested by the police! But why would everyone be happy?

Finally I got the story. Down the river, near my forest-clearing site, railway work went on through the winter. At a place called Maple Ridge, Chinese workers were badly treated by their crew boss. Two men fought with him, and he went to a judge. A police constable seized the two Chinese and was taking them to town when they passed a Chinese crew. These workers tried to free the arrested men, so the constable pushed his two prisoners into a store. The Chinese crew surrounded the store with their axes and shovels. They banged and shouted and threatened to tear down the building. Inside, two frightened Red Beards urged the constable to release the prisoners, and finally he agreed. The two freed men ran off with the work crew.

The judge then asked the Sto:lo people along the river to watch for the two escaped prisoners. Soon the two men came looking for a boat to take them to Second City. But the local people seized them and handed them to the judge. The judge fined the two prisoners $15 each. After paying their fines, the men went back to work.

People were happy with the end of the story: the men paid a small fine and went back to work. And none of the workers who had chased the constable were arrested.

My trip back to camp was a happy one. I hoped Ba's case could be quickly resolved, to let life get back to normal. My tent-mates crowed that we should never fear challenging crew bosses. I was not so sure. They carry guns under their vests.

February 19

Old Fire predicted it would rain today. His almanac called for "spring showers." And it rained! I will believe in the Chinese calendar if it brings warm weather faster.

Blind Eye's term ended today. A month remains before work starts. We debated who should take the next term. Thunder God has a bad knee and Saltwater Crisp is still weak. Should we draw lots? Should we each do a week? Did anyone want to volunteer?

Thunder God shouted out, "I'll pay one of you to do my term."

The men looked at me because I was the youngest. I pointed out that my family had two members here. In the end, we all agreed Tiger Face should earn the money.

My family greatly needs the money, but I refuse to do that horrible job again.

February 23

Saltwater Crisp is better. He helped fetch water. He asked me to write a letter to his mother. He promised to return to China this year. He claimed to be in fine health, having survived the long winter. This time, he said, he would be ready to get married. I was surprised a man of his age had no wife. Of course, I dared not ask him about this.

February 24

Tiger Face came back from town and said that Hot Water Wing said that ever since the news about Maple Ridge, his Red Beard customers had treated him rudely. A few had not picked up their laundry. Hot Water Wing worried that other Red Beards would not pay their accounts because they were angry at how Chinese had disrespected their laws.

February 25

There was thunderous crashing from far off. The rains were loosening great packs of snow at the top of mountains. I didn't understand why it would be so loud. Snow fell soft and lightly, did it not? Old Fire explained that when the snow pack began to slide, it moved like a solid wall that tore down trees and pulled out boulders and carried them down the mountain, pounding and bouncing against everything in its way.

February 28

Yesterday, the tent flap went up in the middle of the day and a dark figure barged in. It was not one of us, because all the tent-mates were present. The lack of light left us blind. Some renegade had come to rob us! Then a familiar voice barked out, "Rock Brain, why didn't you visit me?"

I jumped to my feet. "I tried," I stammered, "but it was too cold. My feet got wet. And people warned me that a cougar was prowling in the area."

Ba dismissed my explanations and called me lazy, while the men loudly demanded to hear his story. I wanted to leave, but I was as curious as the others. Ba went before a judge for trial, where a businessman from Yale translated for him. When Contractor did not show up to testify, the judge sent an officer to Chinatown. The merchants there said Contractor had sailed to China. So the case was dismissed. What a waste, I thought.

Thunder God chuckled and called Ba lucky for having been fed and kept warm all winter in jail, without paying a penny. Ba grumbled about being locked up with no one to talk to and nothing but a water bucket to watch. He bragged about all the books he knew: *Three Word Classic*, *Thousand Word Essay*, *Three Hundred Tang Poems*. He had recited them all to himself, over and over.

For me, this was a first time, to hear Ba assert that he had been schooled.

"So now you can teach school?" The men laughed.

Tiger Face stoked the stove and made tea. I offered to go fetch water. I went as far away as possible and came back as slowly as possible.

March 1

I awoke early, and went to the latrine. To my surprise, Ba was already there. He grunted that he had eaten too much fine food last night. Fine food? Here? Hah! Then he surprised me further by reporting how the men had praised me.

They mentioned how I had gone to town to get berries for Saltwater Crisp's scurvy, how I had chopped bed logs for them, and how I had struggled to reach Yale in a snowstorm, even though I was sick from spoiled food.

"Glad to hear this," Ba grunted. "I did not think you would survive the winter. I know you hate it here."

I shrugged. What else could I do? But it warmed me to hear that he was pleased, for once!

Before I could ask about our debt, he was gone. I guess being jailed did him good! Maybe he missed me! Maybe he had time to ponder our family problems.

March 2

The snow and ice are melting rapidly. I can see the dirt trail now. I want work to start soon, so that Ba can see me at work. In the meantime, many visitors want to hear about Ba's ordeal in jail, so he gets plenty of talk time.

Ba asked my tent-mates about the winter here, and they chuckled about the mice, the burnt rice, and my frostbite. Everyone was in a jolly mood, which I had not seen for a long while. Was that due to Ba? Saltwater Crisp vowed to eat more vegetables. Thunder God showed his blackened knee. Old Fire and Blind Eye claimed they enjoyed having young folk in the tent. That was Tiger Face and me. "If anything happened," Blind Eye said, "we knew the young ones would save us."

Both Tiger Face and I were embarrassed.

March 4

When I gave Ba the letter that had come for Poy Uncle, he demanded to know why I hadn't opened it.

Ba was being rude as usual but I decided to be polite. I reminded him that Poy Uncle was his friend, and that I was just a boy.

"You're right." He sighed. "This is my responsibility."

I mentioned the letter from Ma that I had forwarded to Yale. He had received it, so I asked, "Did you write back to her?"

He did not reply.

March 6

Old Fire's almanac says in three days it will be Insects Awaken. Therefore he predicts that railway work will resume soon. I pray he is right.

March 8

The Company man came and told us to be ready to move tomorrow. The men groaned at the thought of going back to work, but I wanted to jump for joy. We all need to earn money!

The Company man looked at Thunder God's knee and shook his head. "No use for you to come along," he said. "You go down to Yale."

Thunder God has not spoken a word since then, nor has he eaten anything. Later, Ba went to him, and they chatted late into the night.

March 11, near Fargus Bar, British Columbia

After three cold months, men from five crews have assembled to form a new gang. No one is friendly; there are few prospects for new friends. Maybe they ate the same bitter food all winter, so now they are sullen and sour. One crew contained men all surnamed Zhou. In another, the men were all from Jung-San. Already borders are drawn between them and people from Toi-San. We asked if anyone had worked at this place last year. People shook their heads.

In my opinion, this site is the best so far. It is the farthest point to which the railway has been built. Unfortunately that point (called the railhead) sits inside a tunnel. This morning we entered with lanterns, baskets and shovels. As daylight faded behind us, our voices echoed around us. The train stood like a statue in a deserted temple. Cars stretched behind it, loaded with gravel. The engine was quiet and still, but warm.

"Don't touch it," someone hissed. "Red Beards call this machine Satan. It was standing on a rail being repaired when it suddenly lurched and rolled ahead and injured the machinist."

We jumped onto the cars and shovelled stone into our baskets. Once they were full, we pushed the stone onto the ground so the train could leave right away and fetch more. Then we started to extend the roadbed by building a layer of gravel fifteen feet wide and two feet high.

Before we finished shovelling the first load, more stone arrived. Already? So fast? Old Fire said the second train had likely been waiting nearby, so the first train and its empty cars went off the main track to let the second train pass. I heard it coming and wanted to drop my baskets and run back to see, but Bookman was standing right by me. I had no choice but to keep jogging to the end of the roadbed.

At day's end, everyone muttered about sore backs and aching muscles. Old Fire bent over to wash but could barely straighten himself. Blind Eye lay down and refused to get up for dinner.

Me, I felt fine. Last year, we had chopped trees and removed mountains. But here I was building something instead of tearing things down.

March 13

Ba brought his dinner bowl over and slipped me a package.

"For you," he said, looking sheepish, "to mark one year in Canada."

I frowned. Had that much time passed? Of course I made no fuss in front of the men. Later I checked my journal to see if Ba had gotten the right date. Yes, we left China a year ago. How had he remembered? He never looked at calendars. The gift was a carrying case made of palm-leaf straw, with a shoulder strap. Clearly it was for my box of journals.

His jail cell, Ba said, was empty except for two Chinese fans. They had been well used by the summer prisoners because the room had no windows and enjoyed no shade outside. Ba took apart the dusty fans and rewove the fibres. I had no idea he knew how to weave straw.

"Nothing to do, squatting in jail," he said curtly. "It was a living death. Besides, what would I do with two fans in the winter?"

Exercise your wrists? I almost said.

Then I wondered if Ba had softened while in jail.

March 15

Last night, we woke to the panicked shouts of men. Instantly I was alert, my heart pounding, my ears cocked for any crackle of danger. Someone beat a tin box and made dull thuds while another person banged pot lids together. Ba and Saltwater Crisp pulled on their boots and ran outside. By the time I got outside, lanterns had been lit and the entire crew was aroused. The tent next to ours lay flat on the ground; its occupants were huddled around, shivering from cold and fright.

One man had woken to a foul smell and heard low grunts. Something had breathed warm air onto him. When his hand touched thick smooth fur, he screamed, "Wild beast!"

Everyone had awakened and joined him yelling and banging. The worst part, they said, was not being able to see. There were scratching and clawing sounds, growling, the strong smell and a huge careening shadow. The animal finally turned and plunged through one wall of the tent, dragging it down. Old Fire said bears rarely woke up from their long sleep so early in the year, so something or someone must have disturbed it. It scares me how nothing seems to follow rules out here.

Tiger Face suggested that we leave a lantern burning through the night.

"That will attract more bugs!" we cried.

March 18

The day was not warm but I went along the river, looking for a fishing spot. I passed a stream where

Nlaka'pamux people were fishing. They looked friendly, so I waved and called out "Kla How Ya," which Old Fire said was a greeting in their language. I hope Old Fire was right, because no-one replied. Maybe I said it badly. I went farther up the river, and it took a while to reach another stream. But the Red Beards fishing there glared at me and shouted out angry words. I was eager to fish, so I went around them and climbed farther up the stream. Red Beards tie their lines to long poles, so it is easy to see when they are going fishing. I carried no pole, so nobody knew what I was doing. A well-worn path followed the river bank, so Nlaka'pamux people were nearby. Jerky movements in the shallow water made me smile.

I dug around for bait, and threw my line into the water. It was not long before a fish got hooked. I killed it, checked for blood and covered it with fat green leaves. Soon I had several fish to take to Cook. We are eating the mushy rice and dried salmon again, but Cook tries very hard to add flavours with pickles, sauces and spicy preserves.

March 19

The train brought larger gravel for us to cover the smaller rocks in a layer just as thick. Bookman ordered us to look closely in our baskets, to make sure we dumped the right rocks in the right place. Too bad most of the crew does not respect him.

Bookman insisted we march on top of the gravel as we trot with our baskets to the roadbed's end. That point moved farther and farther away from the train with every trip we made. Our feet sank and twisted into the gravel. Blind Eye tripped and overturned his baskets of rock. Luckily, there was no need to recover the spill.

Soon I saw why Bookman wanted us walking there. Men took shovels and hammers to pound at the rock to flatten the layers. When the rock flew out the two sides, it was shovelled up and dumped back onto the trop. The gravel of the roadbed must settle firmly and hold itself together.

March 21

People are smiling because most of them, including Ba, paid off their ship tickets this payday. I should be smiling too, but I learned a bitter truth today. I am not earning much money. When Bookman showed me my account, I almost fell over. He was taking $27.41 off for rental of the tent and for my winter clothes. I should have spent less at the Company store. Turns out Ba did not pay my winter costs; it had been all talk. So I had to assign $20.30 to Old Fire for the food and fuel. My total earnings fell to $18.74, a third of what I had before!

What a disaster.

It was as if I had just arrived in Canada and worked only a month.

I do not know how the others felt, but I wanted to weep. I was worthless. I was a dishrag. It would be better to walk into the forest and freeze to death.

I went to Ba and told him about my account. I expected him to yell at me for being stupid. Instead, he looked at me curiously and asked if I had any idea how much was owed. When I guessed a hundred dollars, he roared with laughter.

"If someone gave me a hundred dollars for my railway wages," he said, "I would grab it and run to Mexico!"

Ba told me flatly that no-one earned much on this job. Gamblers knew this and only lent small amounts. Ba said our total debt was thirty dollars. Of course we would be able to pay it off and have money to take home. I couldn't believe it. I had worried uselessly for a year! I could have slept soundly at night instead! I wanted to kick myself. I really had been a Rock Brain.

Later

I still cannot believe what an idiot I am. The worst part is, there is no-one to blame but ME. I thought

Ba's debt must be as big as Grandfather's. Now I feel like an old man, tired and beaten up.

March 22

Tonight, a Jung-San man snarled loudly, "Don't know why the Zhou people always get the easy jobs. Do they pay money to Bookman, or does Bookman prefer his kinsmen over us?"

Those were fighting words. When I thought about the accusation, it was true. The men who flattened the roadbed were always the Zhou fellows. The rest of us trekked back and forth between the railhead and the end of the roadbed. We were the ones wearing out our shoe leather.

"Why are Jung-San people so stupid?" retorted a Zhou. "They go to work where no-one knows them, where everyone comes from Say-Yup. If they were from Say-Yup, then they would get the good jobs too."

Liar! Nobody from our crowd had gotten a turn at flattening the roadbed.

"Don't get up," Saltwater Crisp whispered to me. "Don't say a word."

A Jung-San man grabbed a shovel and rushed at the Zhous. We all jumped up and looked for weapons, but Cook shouted and stepped in, brandishing his cleaver.

"If there's a problem, let's talk it over slowly," he

said soothingly. "We're all workers here, why fight among ourselves?"

Ba shook his head. "This happened in the first crew that I worked with," he said.

March 23

Cook is surnamed Zhou too but he dislikes how Bookman plays favourites. Today, the jobs were given out fairly. Even I got a chance to flatten the roadbed. It felt wonderful to use my entire body to swing a hammer, and to hear a satisfying *whumph* hit the ground.

At dinner, Cook served a treat: dried vegetables.

"It's too early for fresh greens," he declared. "I do the best I can for everyone."

Everyone received equal portions. Then Cook told a funny story with a lesson:

> People in the Yee family were very proud, always bragging about how smart they were. After his first day at school, Ah-Choy came home and told his mother, "Teacher told us to stand up and recite the *Three Word Classic.* I knew twenty verses but the other children only knew five. Is that because I am a Yee?"
>
> "No, my son," Ma said. "It is because you listen to your mother."

> Ah-Choy said, "Teacher told us to stand up and say our numbers. I counted up to 50 but the other children only reached 15. Is that because I am a Yee?"
>
> "No, my son," Ma said. "It is because you listen to your mother."
>
> Ah-Choy said, "Teacher lined up all the students, and I was three times taller than the other children. Is that because I am a Yee?"
>
> "No, my son," Ma said. "It is because you are twenty-seven years old."

Everyone laughed. Good thing there was no one surnamed Yee in our crew.

March 24

I have not had a week such as this since leaving China. Two pieces of good news, side by side, since three days ago!

When we returned to camp today, a familiar face waited for Ba and me. Ox Uncle was grinning from ear to ear. He was so excited he couldn't sit still. He had spent the winter in Second City, in a busy boarding house. A fellow boarder was Old Jang, the gambler to whom both Ox Uncle and Ba owed money.

When work resumed this spring, Old Jang and Ox Uncle landed in the same gang. Last week Old

Jang received a letter, telling him both his parents had died suddenly. The father died from illness and then, three days later, the mother never woke up. The coincidence spooked the entire family. Everyone in the village said the couple must have offended the gods somehow. Now the family was carrying out cleansing rituals in China.

Right away Old Jang did charity to address his parents' misdeeds. He donated money to the Chinese hospital in Yale. He bought a ship ticket for Kwan-somebody who lost both his legs in an accident. And he cancelled Ba and Ox Uncle's debts. Both men were overjoyed. Me too! They slapped each other on the back, and Ox Uncle pulled out a jug of wine to celebrate with. They called themselves the luckiest men in Gold Mountain!

Ba grinned and asked if I was pleased.

"Only if you stop gambling," I blurted. Did he not see how blessed he was? He had been granted a gift, for doing absolutely nothing! He could have lost everything, but now his fortune was reversed! Surely this was a sign from the gods that he should mend his ways!

When he shook his head, I urged him to put aside some of his winnings so that he didn't lose all his money again and again. He didn't hear me.

He was too busy laughing with Ox Uncle. Still, I guess I will sleep better tonight.

March 25

Saltwater Crisp went to town and picked up a letter. His wife advised that the second crop last year had been very poor, due to a lack of rainfall. Ba confirmed that Poy Uncle's wife had reported the same news in her letter. She and Ah-Wing had struggled to bring in the rice, but the yield was low while the labour needed to harvest the grain was the same as always. They had to keep all the grain for food so there was none to sell and no income for the household.

Everyone looked sad, so Cook told a joke:

> A scholar going to Beijing passes through a small town and hears the clanging of gongs, the *crack-crack-crack* of firecrackers, and the loud weeping of hired mourners. A fancy funeral parades by, with waving flags and banners and people tossing spirit money all around. The costly fuss is clearly for someone very important.
>
> "What great man passed away?" calls out the scholar.
>
> A spectator points to the coffin. "The one in there."

Later, I asked Ba if I should send money to Poy Aunty. He said he had taken care of things already.

March 27

The train brought important supplies and we eagerly unloaded them. We were handling real pieces of the iron road! Finally we were going to build the railway! We became polite and helpful, calling out to one another in the dark, "Be careful," "Grab it here," or "Watch your step there."

"Don't drop it!" called out one joker. "It may break! You'll pay for damages!"

The 8-foot-long wooden ties had two flat sides and two unfinished sides that still showed tree bark. Two men could carry a wooden tie, but eight men were needed for a steel rail. It was rusty, 30 feet long and weighed 600 pounds. Everyone watched their step, so we moved slowly. If the rail slipped from our grasp, eight men could be injured all at once!

We unloaded heavy sacks of metal spikes, connector-plates and bolts. Some bags weighed as much as the wooden ties.

We put the ties by the roadbed, lining them up like rows of soldiers. Tiger Face tripped over a tie and fell with a crash. The sound was from the lantern he carried, but in the tunnel, everything sounded louder.

March 28

The trains delivered several loads of rock, so we did more unloading. It was hard to keep my gaze off the ties and rails, and I stumbled several times. I imagined carefully guiding the wood and steel into place, pounding the spikes through them, and twisting the bolts tight as a final touch. I wanted to push something into the earth, and then watch it grow, like seedlings planted in springtime.

Maybe Crew Boss was waiting for a sunny day before starting.

March 29

The train delivered a huge contraption of metal blades, which teams of horses dragged over the roadbed. The heavy blades squealed as they scraped and scratched their way over the stone. After they passed by, the roadbed looked smooth and level.

Then the Red Beard workers who had come with the horses started work. We Chinese set the wooden ties in place on the roadbed. Some of us held the lanterns closer to let Crew Boss see clearly. He used a marked rope to ensure the distance between each tie was the same. Then we assembled on both sides of the roadbed, slowly lifted two steel rails, and gradually lowered them onto the wooden ties. Everyone was alert and there was much shouting in order to get the two rails to land at the same time. This way, the ties did not buckle and all the weight settled in a balanced way into the roadbed.

Crew Boss used another rope to set the distance between the two rails, and we adjusted their final placement.

But once everything was in place, the Red Beard workers did all the work.

I turned away, very disappointed. I was a donkey laden with heavy sacks, or an ox ploughing thick mud. No need to think, just move along, move along, move along.

Tiger Face would not look me in the face, so he must have felt as I did. Later I was embarrassed at having assumed we would do the job. But it did not look that difficult.

March 31

After the rails were laid, the Red Beards mounted a sturdy metal cart over them. The cart flew along as two men aboard it pumped a see-saw up and down to provide power. At one spot, the men stopped and called for us to lay more gravel onto the roadbed and to pack it down hard.

Now the train can pass through the tunnel and

travel a short distance outside. Now we can see the engine clearly in the daylight.

April 1

Ching Ming occurs in seven days, so teams of men went into the forest looking for graves. We figured Chinese must be buried nearby, because we had all worked on similar stretches of the iron road where deadly accidents had happened.

The Zhou team returned first, having found markers for two persons surnamed Lee and Chan. Ba and our kinsmen Lees asked to be first to present offerings at the grave. But the Zhous insisted on going first because they had located the site. As we argued, a foul-mouthed Zhou fellow told us to stop sitting around like ladies and go find our own site. Good thing another team came back with news of a Zhou and a Hoy person buried beside a Red Beard.

Luckily our rest day falls on the actual day of Ching Ming. Ba asked me to go out early that morning and catch some fish. Then he disappeared into the gambling tent. Every time he gambles, I worry he will lose our money again.

April 2

I feel very proud when the train comes through the tunnel and stops at the railhead. All those cars were travelling on something that my hands had built!

The Red Beards worked on the rest day, putting up a machine at the railhead. It burns wood in a tank that also holds water. Every now and then, the engineer releases steam in short, powerful bursts from under the sturdy frame of logs.

When a load of stone arrived, this time we lined our baskets alongside the cars. Long metal cables led from the steam-maker all the way to the end of the train. I noticed it had fewer cars than usual. On the last car, a huge piece of steel, curved and smooth like a plough, and as wide as the train, was thrust under the load of stone.

Someone blew a whistle, and the steam-maker turned grunting gears and wheels. They tightened the metal cables which in turn dragged the great plough forward, making it work like a giant shovel. As it chugged ahead, the load of gravel slid along the curved sides and then down, to fall off the car and into our waiting baskets. The plough slid from one car to the next, pushing and forcing the stone off the cars. In no time, all the cars were clear and the train backed away.

We dug out our baskets and carried them to the roadbed. More than half the gravel had spilled off the train and landed on the ground, but still the unloading had taken much less time and the trains would return sooner.

The Red Beards shook the hands of one Red Beard man and clapped him on the shoulder. He had been scribbling into a notebook all this time. Bookman said he was a top boss from very high up in the Company. He had recently been hired to speed up the work and to save money for the Company. When I mentioned that he looked familiar, Bookman said Top Boss constantly inspected the line and workers. Top Boss rode off on his own horse; he did not wait for the train to give him a ride.

That is what being powerful means: you never wait for anything.

April 4

Now that rock is unloaded so quickly, another crew of Chinese arrived to help build up the roadbed. I had hoped to see familiar faces from my earlier crews, but no such luck. The newcomers were friendly and came to chat with us. One fellow told us about the big fire in Guang Zhou last year. Eight hundred houses were burned, and there were fierce battles between looters and soldiers.

April 6

The Jung-San men complained about Bookman giving the easy work to his fellow Zhou kinsmen. Bookman pretended to be innocent.

"I hadn't noticed this was going on," he declared. "If anything unfair is happening, it is accidental. Truly! I'll make sure this does not happen again."

What a liar!

April 8

I went to the nearby stream early this morning but failed to catch any fish. They were probably still sleeping. Then I managed to find a hard-to-see trail that led back to near our camp. I am a genius!

Cook had brought back two live chickens from town. He cooked them yesterday, so both groups had one for their offerings. Cook also purchased incense and candles and spirit money.

Everyone was dismayed at the sight of the grave markers. One name had been brushed onto the wood long ago, and then someone had cut into the wood with a knife, tracing the outline of the brush strokes. The ink had washed away, and the only way to read the marker was to pull it out and hold it at a certain angle to the light.

On the other marker, the name Lee Yiu-nam, from San Lei village in Toi-San, had been scratched on faintly with a dull knife. Again, the winter was eating away the words. Soon, nothing would show on the marker, which had split down its centre. Lee Yiu-nam was only twenty-one years old when he died.

We Lees decided to make a new marker for our kinsman. The words would be brushed onto wood in ink, and then cut in deeply with knife and pick. We would oil the wood to protect it. There was no guarantee the marker would last seven years, but it was the best we could do. Someone suggested getting a railway tie to use as a marker, but we had no saws for cutting it down to the right size.

April 9

I can hardly write properly. My hands are shaking from what I just learned.

After dinner, Ba told me to walk with him. We strode away from the camp. He quietly told me that when he and Poy Uncle first saw the dangers of railway work, they made a vow. They promised each other that if one of them got killed, then the other man would return to China and care for the other man's family. Ba told me he had delayed going back while trying to earn more money for everyone. Now his conscience bothers him. He says he was wrong to stay longer. Last night, he saw Poy Uncle in a dream, calling from a boat out on the ocean. Ba said we should return to China soon.

I reminded him how he was the one who thought we should work here so that in the future, Chinese people could live in this country. He looked away. He didn't know I had heard that, he said. Now that Poy Uncle was gone, he wasn't sure it was worthwhile.

For ninety-five per cent of my time in Canada, I have longed to go home. Suddenly I was not sure. "The work is not as dangerous as before," I said cautiously. "No one has died at this work site. We will not get hurt, doing this work."

Ba curtly reminded me of his promise, so I stopped talking. No point in arguing when it comes to deals made with ghosts. At the end, he sighed and said that we would wait and see.

April 11

It is as if Ba and I never talked two days ago. Our people are muttering angrily. Bookman kept his so-called promise to be fair for two days, but now his kinsmen are getting all the easy jobs again. Ba went with the Jung-San fellow to complain to Bookman. This time, he blamed us for the problem!

"You people are never around when I need you!"

he shouted. "You're always clumped together, chatting among yourselves, far down the line. You should pay attention to the work around you. You should know when it's time to change workers. That's when you should come to me. What am I supposed to do? Chase you down with a gold-engraved invitation?"

"If things don't get better," Ba declared, "then we're going to complain to Contractor."

Old Fire and Saltwater Crisp clapped Ba on the back and said, "Well done!"

April 12

A worker in the second Chinese crew is having a hard time with his crew boss. He is surnamed Liang, and every time he passes Short Boss, Short Boss will call out in English and make the Red Beards laugh. Liang is short and slight, and his two front teeth stick out. He wears a Western vest and always looks neat. I think he has been teased all his life, but it should end for a grown man.

Today Short Boss grabbed Liang's queue and pulled. Liang stumbled to the ground, and Short Boss yanked him up. Liang cried out in pain. His friends ran up, and Short Boss backed off, holding up his palms. But he was laughing all the while.

April 14

Top Boss rode in again, followed by two horses. One carried a Red Beard in a stiff suit, and the other was loaded with small equipment. Bookman reported that he was a photographer come to take pictures of the stone-unloading machine. It had been invented by Top Boss after he started working on this railway.

We stood to the side and waited. The Red Beard workers posed in front of the engine, the cars and the stone-unloading machine. They thrust their thumbs under their suspenders and puffed out their chests. At one point the photographer shouted to the engineer to stop the plough. We had never seen it stop halfway through its scraping. The photographer took many pictures and moved his camera around. He pointed at us, but the Crew Bosses shook their heads and pulled him away.

April 17

Ba showed me a letter he had picked up in town. Ma has more bad news. Little Brother refuses to look at his books. Instead, he runs around with a trio of wild boys. They go to town and loiter on the busy street, hoping that a vendor will toss them a treat or that a merchant might pay one to run an errand. When they get into people's way, they get scolded.

Aunty Stinky told Ma to sell her few pieces of gold and jade. Ma snapped back, "These are for Heen-gwong's bride."

Aunty Stinky embarrassed Ma at the temple. During First of Winter, Aunty Stinky tipped the temple keeper but said the money was only from her and her sister. Ma had no money and was left red-faced.

Grandfather swears he quit gambling, but Ma's neighbours tell her differently. She cannot challenge him, so she wants Ba to go home and do so. She also mentioned how the poor winter harvest had pushed up the price of rice.

Ba reminded me that we would leave soon. I stomped off without saying a word, refusing to encourage him. If he wants to go home, then he should stop gambling and protect his savings.

April 19

We were taking a rest and Cook's assistant brought us huge kettles of cooled boiled water. Helper was pouring a scoopful for Liang when Short Boss walked up. He had a metal mug, so of course Helper filled it. Then Short Boss held it out to Liang. Liang did not understand and looked around in confusion. Short Boss stood patiently, waiting for an answer. When Liang finally nodded, Short Boss poured the water over Liang. Everyone laughed and said he should not have nodded. He should have run off instead.

April 20

We have extended the roadbed quite a distance, but more ties and rails did not come until today.

As the Red Beards spike the long rails to the ties, the ringing echoes of steel on steel fill the air like hundreds of blacksmiths hammering. Nothing can be heard over the noise. It is deafening, and I think everyone's eardrums are hurt or they are getting headaches.

Pairs of men face each other over the rail but they work as one. The first man slams his hammer onto the spike. While he swings his hammer around for the next blow, his partner bangs the same spike. Each man swings his hammer wide to get solid power behind it, but they never miss the spike, never hit one another. Instead, they create their own steady rhythm. After a while, the sound seems to be part of nature, rising out of the ground. Spikes go in on both sides of a rail, tight against the steel, so that the rail will stay in place for the trains. The men are accurate but they are amazingly quick. A count of fifteen will see a spike installed. When the shrill whistle announces a break, the sudden silence is as shocking as when I dive off a crowded bridge into a deep river.

I asked Old Fire why we could not do track-laying.

"The Company must employ Red Beard workers too," he replied. "If it used only Chinese workers, Canadians would complain. They don't want their taxes making us rich."

"Rich?" I sputtered. "Nobody gets rich working like this."

April 21

Today I let out a big breath of relief! I finished paying for my ship ticket. I earned $12.98 this month, the second highest amount so far.

Ba earned $15.40 this month, so I am doing well by comparison. So far my total is $31.72 and Ba has $45.50. If I hadn't gotten sick, I would have more money than him. I asked Ba if we had enough to pay for tickets back to China and to pay off Grandfather's debt. Ba shook his head, so I proposed that we work another month here. He agreed reluctantly. I didn't let out a cheer until I was deep in the woods by myself. I should have proposed he stop gambling too, but that would have been impossible.

I also whispered a prayer to Poy Uncle, begging him to understand our situation.

April 22

I was busy writing letters today, so I did not get away to fish. Some men describe Bookman's unfair treatment in their letters. Others talk about the pretty springtime, with wildflowers blooming everywhere. They complain about the food and recall dishes from home. They mention how we observed Ching Ming here, with all the proper rituals. Other people have family troubles, just like us.

One man was in a rush and would not think about what to say. "Just write the same words you put down for the fellow before me," he said. "I'll pay you the same, even though it's easier for you since you've already written it once before."

It is strange that I have written so many letters, but never one for myself. How could I? As long as Ba was here, only the household head could report matters to Grandfather and Ma. I could only write to Little Brother, and why would I waste my time on him?

But if I was to write to him now, then I would say this spring season differs from all other springs that I have known. I saw the land change, from blinding white to green shades and flower colours. The giant fire car ran over the iron road that I helped to lay. Suddenly I believe that anything is possible. Maybe we *will* build a railway in China. Ba's debt was a dark cloud. I will never make that mistake again, rush to believe something without the facts. If Little Brother wants to grow up quickly, then he should come here.

April 23

There was no work for us. The train did not deliver stone, and we had flattened the roadbed several times. Bookman and Crew Boss shrugged and said nothing could be done. Rain fell all day and we huddled under the trees to stay dry.

April 24

A few days ago, a Lee kinsman went and loudly praised Bookman's handwriting. Then Bookman agreed to do the brushwork for the grave marker. He really has a fine hand, which is surprising because Teacher says you can tell from a man's brushwork if he is kind-hearted or not. A Lee in another tent started carving the words but cut his thumb badly. His job landed on me. Tiger Face offered to help, even though he is not a Lee. I will take it to work, in case there are more delays.

April 26

Short Boss stuck out his foot when Liang passed by and tripped him. Then Short Boss pretended to be surprised and helped him to his feet. Liang's palms and knees were cut and bloodied, and he angrily shook off Short Boss. Bookman told us he had warned Crew Boss that a fight will erupt if Short Boss does not stop bullying Liang.

Bookman urged us to work faster. "Don't let the track-laying machine catch up to you," he said. "Then Red Beards will stand there and watch your every move."

"Let's switch jobs," Old Fire called out. "If the Red Beards are so strong and fast, let them extend the roadbed instead. We Chinese will lay the tracks!"

April 27

We finished carving the marker today, thanks to several delays at work. Cook gave us oil to rub into the wood. Ba will return the marker on the next rest day. He worries we kept it away for too long and may have angered the dead man.

Ba was never home for funerals, so I never knew his view of them. Some men call them a waste of time. Others fear them and hide from death processions. No-one close to me ever died. The men who died here were the closest. I never saw how death affected people the way it changed Ba. I know now that Ba must return to China. Problem is, I am more and more sure that I do not want to go.

I did a count of deaths and accidents, and discovered that all the incidents that I recorded in my journal occurred last year. In the seven weeks of this year's work, we have been safe. This latest job is safer: no falling trees, no explosives, no boulders falling from high up. I pray we do not get moved back to do tunnel work again.

April 28

Liang wears a hat to protect his queue but that did not stop Short Boss from harassing him. Short Boss grabbed his cap, a very nice hat, and dangled it in front of Liang. When he lunged for it, Short Boss threw it to his buddy. The two Red Beards tossed it between them, laughing as Liang jumped in vain to intercept the hat. Finally our crew boss marched in, grabbed the hat and handed it back to its owner.

April 30

This is a strange country. The newest gambling involves the railway! Somehow, our two Chinese bookmen started to race our crew bosses on the handcar, to see who could pump it to go faster. Of course they cannot race side by side because there is only one track and one handcar. Instead, one pair takes a run on the handcar. At the finish line, their time is recorded. Two timekeepers use two watches to keep everyone honest. The pair who wins two out of the three races is declared winner.

In both the Chinese and Red Beard camps, money was collected as men wagered on who would win. To everyone's surprise, the Chinese won the first match two days ago. Many Chinese had bet the Red Beards would win because they look bigger and stronger. Yesterday, a rematch was won by the Red Beards. At camp, everyone is talking about the races, trying to explain why the Chinese won at first, and then lost.

The track-laying machine tests the new rails each time it moves forward, so the handcar is not needed for that task. Next time there is a race, I am running over to watch.

May 2

The Chinese contractor scolded us severely. Liang's problems with Short Boss had come to his attention, and he was not happy.

"You are guest workers," he shouted at us. "That's all you are. To Red Beards, you are nothing! Did you know that? They are keen for the railway to be finished, for then you will leave. If you want earnings to take with you, then you should behave properly. You can be fired easily. You can be replaced easily. More Chinese are arriving and asking for railway work, did you know that? If any Red Beard gives you trouble, my advice to you is: stay out of his way! You don't know when the Company may start to discharge workers. It could be soon, or it could be later."

The workers seethed as they listened.

At the end, Contractor said coldly, "I hear of handcar races here. The Company forbids them. Anyone caught racing a handcar will be fired right away."

May 3

The explosion we had all been awaiting erupted today. It was exceptionally hot this afternoon, as hot as China's summer, so that may have set off Liang. He carried two baskets of gravel by Short Boss and his friends. Short Boss called out something that made his little crowd chortle. Liang dropped his load and charged at Short Boss. He moved quickly and picked up a rock and smashed it into Short Boss's face. Blood spurted out from his nose. Short Boss grabbed Liang around the neck and choked him, but Liang kept hitting Short Boss with the rock. The two men kicked viciously at one another. The Red Beards tried to stop the fight but Liang's workmates blocked them.

"Let them fight," they shouted in Chinese. "Only this will end their battle."

The Red Beards saw Liang gaining the upper hand, and pushed their way through. Liang broke free and ran off just in time. Short Boss fell to the ground and his friends carried him away. Crew Boss ordered us back to work.

When we returned to camp, Liang was gone. Bookman had taken him away, to hide him in one of the other camps farther down the river. When Bookman came back, he said the Red Beards would likely invade our camp to beat Liang up. The only way to help him was to help him escape. Then Bookman went to advise the crew bosses that Liang had run away.

May 4

Last night, hardly anyone in our camp slept well. Short Boss was not at the site today, but we continued to extend the roadbed.

A scuffle broke out between some men, but I was too far away to see it. Afterwards, no one wanted to talk about it. Did something shameful happen, or do they think I am too young to hear?

May 6

I finally saw a handcar race! Unlike dragon boat races, there are no drums, no crowds, and no colourful start line. The advantage of using one cart is that no one is tempted to sabotage it. The race happens so quickly that no wonder I missed the first two races.

Chinese gather at one point of the railway, Red Beards at the other. A whistle shrills and the handcar hurtles off. All you hear is the squeal of wheels against steel track. As the car nears the finish line, men chant, "Faster! Faster! Faster!" louder and louder. Then the crowd swamps the timekeepers to get the times. Quickly, the next team boards and the whistle sounds again.

After two races, the Chinese had won both. Then everyone melted away before a third race could be run, in case a high-up boss showed up.

We celebrated at camp. Cook roasted peanuts and jugs of wine were passed about. Then Bookman arrived and announced the Red Beards were issuing a challenge for tomorrow. They dismissed the two-out-of-three win, and wanted a three-out-of-five series. They wanted new men on the handcar. Right away we accepted the challenge. We turned to our biggest, strongest workers, Half Lump and Gold Coin, but they shook their heads.

"We're too big," they said. "Our weight will slow down the cart."

Not everyone wanted to race. Some feared getting caught and fired. Others feared the Red

Beards would beat them up. The most eager volunteers were not always suitable: too short, too old or too weak. Our final choice surprised me: Ba and a fellow called Old Wide.

May 7

Ba and Old Wide were defeated by the Red Beards. Now both sides have won the same number of races. Ba has been replaced by someone else for the final race tomorrow.

May 8

At the work site this morning, Crew Boss and Bookman both looked uneasy. The Company had fired one of the Red Beard racers from yesterday. Now Old Wide was dismissed.

Right away, our men called for a strike. Bookman shook his head. "Don't do that," he warned us. "The Company will fire you all. It is determined to stop handcar racing."

Ba strode away with Old Wide and I ran after them in a panic. When I asked Ba what he intended to do, he said he planned to go to town and ask Contractor to give Old Wide back his job.

"What if he fires you too?" I demanded.

Ba shrugged and said we were planning to quit anyway.

"Not me," I said quietly.

Ba stared at me. Then he said, "Son, now you know how I felt during my first year on the railway. But this year, things are different."

And off he went.

May 9

A runner brought horrible news this afternoon. We knew something strange had happened, because in the middle of the morning, our crew bosses started carrying long guns and wearing guns on their belts. They grunted rudely at us, and when Bookman asked what was wrong, they refused to answer. Short Boss was seen shooting at bottles placed on a tree stump.

The runner blurted his news to our bookmen and then ran on to the next camp. Bookman summoned us. Be on guard against a Red Beard attack, he said. A fight had resulted in a Chinese worker being killed by Red Beards.

It happened at Camp 37, a few miles south of the big Chinatown at Lytton, early yesterday morning. At the work site, a crew boss fired two Chinese workers. Their bookman asked for a quarter day's pay for them. The crew boss refused and tried to leave. The bookman reached out to stop him but fell. The Chinese crew saw this and hurled rocks at the crew boss. Red Beard workers pulled him to safety but the angry Chinese attacked with picks and shovels and crowbars. The Red Beards managed to escape, and then work resumed for the rest of the day.

That night, twenty to thirty Red Beards crept to the Chinese camp and set four cabins on fire. When the Chinese ran out, they were beaten severely with poles and sticks. Yee Fook died and six others were badly wounded.

Right away, we wanted to stop work and make our anger known to the Company. A strike would force the Company to punish the murderers. The crew bosses saw us milling about and pulled aside Bookman. They told him the Company could not punish the killers; that was the duty of the law courts. We went back to work, but everyone was grumbling.

I pray Ba and Old Wide are safe, travelling by themselves on the railway line.

May 10

This morning, Ba shook me awake and told me to pack. We would be leaving right away. He was on his knees, rolling his clothes into a blanket.

I jumped to my feet. "We can't run off like cowards, as if we're afraid!"

Ba reminded me that he had an important

promise to keep. He knotted his blanket firmly and stood up. "I accept the will of Heaven in accidents, but not the evil that men commit. This burning and killing is unforgiveable. The Red Beards hate us more than I ever imagined. When Poy Uncle's wife hears about this, she will worry even more."

He stopped at the door of the tent. "I've thought it over. It's up to you, Heen. I won't force you to leave with me. You're old enough to think for yourself. If you want to stay, I won't get angry. I'll give you respect."

Later

Men are talking about having sentries guard the camp at night. They are also raising money to hire a lawyer to pursue the case.

I decided to stay. By working through the rest of the season, I will bring home more money. In the meantime, Ba will take my journals home with him. He says they will be safer in China. He worries about me, but tries not to show it. I look forward to re-reading my journals when I get home.

I want to send my accounts back to China with my journals, so I went to Bookman. He gave me the latest numbers, and I took every penny that was mine and sent it home with Ba.

Here is the final tally for my year in Canada:

Item	Rate	Number	Expenses	Totals
Total earnings	$1.00 per day	234 days		$234.00
Ship Ticket	China to Canada		40.00	
Work-time deducted	$0.50	7 times	3.50	
Rent	$0.09 per day	374 days	33.66	
Meals at camp	$0.12 per day	293 days	35.16	
Bookman's fee	$0.01 per day	234 days	2.34	
Winter Food	$0.17 per day	90 days	15.30	
Winter Fuel			5.00	
Boots	$5.00 per pair	3 pairs	15.00	
Blankets	$1.50	2	3.00	
Medicine			4.00	
Pants	$1.50 per pair	3 pairs	4.50	
Shirts	$1.75	4	7.00	
Gloves	$0.55	1	.55	
Socks	$0.40 per pair	6	2.40	
Hats	$0.45	3	1.35	
Sweaters	$0.95	2	1.90	
Scarves	$0.25	2	.50	
Notebooks	$0.10	8	.80	
Pencils	$.04	12	.48	
Candies, soap, etc			4.89	
Taxes			3.00	
Underwear			4.00	
Funeral Goods			3.00	
Total Expenses				191.33
Total Received				42.67

Epilogue

In September of 1883, Jon M. Hayes, David H. Perry and John Gray went on trial for Yee Fook's murder at Camp 37. They were charged with murder, manslaughter and common assault. Perry was acquitted due to lack of evidence. The eleven-person jury, after five minutes of debate, found Hayes and Gray not guilty. Chief Justice Matthew Begbie, who presided at the trial, later suggested that some of the witnesses may have lied.

Thunder God passed through Heen's camp at the end of May. He was sad to have missed seeing Ba. Chinese doctors in Yale had healed his knee, making it possible for him to work again. But in December 1883 Heen was fired, along with Old Fire, Blind Eye, Saltwater Crisp and three thousand other Chinese workers. Most of them had not saved enough money to buy a ticket to China. But Heen had been extra careful all year, saving money for Grandfather, so he had enough to pay his ship's passage. Unfortunately, it is not known what happened to Heen's other journals, if he kept any.

For over thirty years, Wong Brother worked as a miner in northern British Columbia. He trekked long distances in the Omineca, Cassiar and Atlin gold fields and found bits of the precious metal here and there. He managed to send money home so that his father did see a good doctor. He eventually retired in Victoria, B.C.

In China, Heen found he could not resume life as a sixteen-year-old in his hometown. He rejected more schooling because he and Ba had failed to bring home enough money to regain Grandfather's store. Heen wanted to work, but no suitable jobs were nearby. He thought to go overseas but the family said no to North America. Grandfather read Heen's journal and exclaimed, "Thank the Heavens and the Earth that you two returned safely."

Ba found a job doing bookkeeping for the Lee clan. Through this work, he met Ngoon Lee, who had an import-export business in Singapore. In 1884, Ba persuaded his new friend to take Heen to Singapore to work there. Ba and Ma had another child, a girl named Pui-gwong, born in 1885. This time, Ba made sure he stayed close to home, to enjoy her childhood.

Two years later, Ma found a bride for Heen, and he returned to China at age nineteen to marry. He and his wife, Hong-ping, had a first child, a son, in 1888. They named him Hok-yun. After Hok-yun's birth, Heen went back to work in Singapore. Hong-ping and son Hok-yun joined him in 1892, and the family became established there. Over the years, Heen rose through the company ranks to become the firm's general manager and a leader in the community.

When Heen's wife and child joined him in Singapore, Grandfather and Ba also moved. They went to Thailand to work with Grandfather's friend in the rice industry. A year later, Ma brought eight-year-old Pui-gwong to Thailand too.

During his first year back from Canada, Heen told many stories about railway work to Little Brother Gee-gwong, who was nine years old then. He never tired of hearing them. In 1893, when Ma and Little Sister moved to Thailand, Gee-gwong turned nineteen and sailed to Vancouver, the city at the western end of the national railway. He worked in nearby shingle mills and salmon canneries and on ferry boats. But he was a gambler, and was unable to save much money.

Poy Uncle's son Ah-Wing came to Canada at the same time as Gee-gwong. He pooled his savings with other Chinese to open a general store in Vancouver's Chinatown. A dozen years later,

Ah-Wing bought out his partners and became the sole owner. His wife joined him in Canada, and they raised six children. But he was unable to find his father's grave along the Fraser River, even though Heen and Ba had given him directions and a hand-drawn map.

Heen never forgot Canada's landscape or the railway work. He also remembered the bitterly cold winters, and he much preferred the tropical climate of Singapore. He kept his journal all his life, often reading and re-reading his earlier words. Decades later, his great-grandson saved it from a stack of old business ledgers being tossed out.

In 1988, one of Heen's great-great-grandsons, electrical engineer Colin Lee, emigrated with his children (Vincent, age ten, and Crystal, age eight) from Singapore. They settled in Calgary. Colin's family took the train to Vancouver and saw much of the Fraser Canyon that Heen had seen. But they had no idea that their ancestors had worked on the Canadian Pacific Railway.

Historical Note

In 1867, a trip from central Canada to British Columbia took several months of exhausting travel over land.

Eastern Canadians from Ontario, Quebec or the Maritimes who were hurrying to take part in the Cariboo gold rush in the 1860s started their journey by taking trains and steamers into Wisconsin, in the United States. They travelled through to St. Paul, Minnesota, before heading north to Fort Garry (later Winnipeg). From there they travelled in ox carts over 900 miles of prairie to Fort Edmonton. Then they fought their way through the Rocky Mountains.

There was no easier route through the south because the American transcontinental railway wasn't finished yet. By sea, ships from Halifax sailed south and around the South American Horn and then up the west coast of two continents. It too was a long and often a dangerous voyage.

A transcontinental railway would solve this transportation problem. The railway would also stop the Americans from taking all the land of North America, provide Canada's motherland Britain with safe passage to the prized markets of Asia, and cement Canada's place in the British Empire. In 1871, a transcontinental railway was one of the terms by which British Columbia agreed to join the Canadian confederation.

But there were problems with raising money to build the railway, and finding enough labourers to do the work.

In 1881, British Columbia had a population of 49,500. It included 19,500 whites, 25,500 First Nations people, and 4,500 Chinese. Railway construction required a force of at least 10,000 workers.

The shortage of white workers and the high cost of building the Canadian Pacific Railway were two reasons that led to the use of Chinese labour. The first Chinese who worked on the job in British Columbia had experience building railways in the United States. As more labour was needed, Chinese workers began to sail directly from China to take up jobs on the railway.

In China, workers were hired by labour contractors working for Andrew Onderdonk, the American engineer who undertook to build the British Columbia section of the railway for the Canadian government. At this time, the Canadian Pacific Railway Company had not yet been formed.

The Chinese railway workers came from one small part of China, located in the southern province of Guangdong. Their home region had an agricultural base, but it lay close to the major seaports of Guang Zhou (Canton) and Hong Kong. For many decades, the men of south China had travelled overseas to work in southeast Asia, in places such as Singapore and Thailand. The tradition of men working abroad and sending money home to their wives and families was well established. News of the gold rushes in North America, first in California in 1848, and then in British Columbia in 1858, drew Chinese men over the Pacific Ocean by the thousands.

Between 1880 and 1885, about seven thousand Chinese workers arrived in B.C. They did not all stay for the entire railway job. They formed three-quarters of the entire workforce.

Chinese workers received $1.00 to $1.25 a day, while their white counterparts got $2.00 to $2.50. The chief contractor on the railway told Canada's prime minister that if Chinese workers were not used, then the railway would have taken an additional fifteen years to complete.

These workers were used only in British Columbia, where the mountainous terrain made the work extremely difficult and dangerous. The length of the railway in B.C. was approximately 615 kilometres. Andrew Onderdonk's contracts covered the distance from Port Moody (on Burrard Inlet, close to Vancouver) to Craigellachie, where the "Last Spike" was pounded into the ground to join the tracks being built to meet each other from east and west.

A construction supervisor on the Canadian Pacific Railway praised the Chinese workers for being adaptable, obedient, self-reliant and clean-living. He found that the Chinese possessed a great advantage: an ability to look after themselves. This allowed large numbers of workers to be relocated from one work site to another. For example, two thousand Chinese workers could be moved 25 miles (40 km) and be at work on the job within 24 hours. By comparison, to move the same number of white men would have taken a week.

At the beginning of railway construction in British Columbia, Chinese and white workers used human muscle and body weight to push drills and swing hammers into rock. For Chinese crews, drilling and clearing tunnels was part of the task of opening a path for the railway. They pushed through thick forest and solid rock, removing trees and stumps, and clearing away undergrowth and boulders. Their tools were picks, drills, shovels and axes. A shift lasted ten hours, except for tunnelling, which was shorter at eight hours. The work of dynamiting and of erecting woodwork for bridges and tunnels was done by white workers.

Where the railway's path did not tunnel through mountains, it was cut into the sides of mountains. There again, the Chinese removed tonnes of blown-up rock and rubble by manual labour.

The railway path had to be graded; that is, the slope of the road was shaped so that it did not slope too steeply. A gentle angle helped train engines push uphill and prevented them from racing downhill, out of control. Workers doing this work removed rock from mountainsides, dragged rock to fill gullies, and levelled the stone to create a smooth pathway sloping at the right angle.

After the railway's path was cleared and graded, Chinese workers built up the roadbed. First they dug drainage ditches on both sides of the path. Then they covered it with gravel, which helped drainage, controlled weed growth and provided a flat base for the ties and rails. Horses then dragged a heavy scraper over the ballast to flatten it.

As different parts of the railway were finished along the route, Chinese workers were discharged. In December 1883, three thousand Chinese and five hundred white workers were laid off. It was reported that not many of the Chinese possessed enough savings to buy a ship ticket to return to China. Penniless, they suffered terribly, lacking food and shelter.

In the summer of 1884, the Chinese of Victoria, B.C., formed the Chinese Benevolent Association, partly in response to anti-Chinese racism and partly to help their fellow countrymen. The following year, many Chinese returned home, though a few moved east of the Rockies to settle in Alberta. Some settled in towns along the Fraser River.

With the completion of the railway, the winter of 1885–1886 took a heavy toll on the unemployed Chinese workers. At least two persons starved to death in the Fraser Valley. Many flooded the Chinatowns of New Westminster and Victoria. The provincial and federal governments refused to help these needy Chinese, so Chinese merchants and organizations stepped in to do the job.

The estimates of how many Chinese workers died during this job range from 600 to 1500, with one estimate as high as 2200. In 1891, the Chinese Benevolent Association sent out teams of men who collected more than 300 unidentified bodies from the Fraser and Thompson River canyons and sent them back to China for burial.

There is a saying that one Chinese worker died for every mile of track laid. The length of railway that the Chinese worked on in British Columbia was 615 kilometres (382 miles). Even the lowest estimate of Chinese workers' deaths backs up this wretched observation.

White British Columbians did not treat the Chinese equally or fairly. Anti-Chinese feelings existed even before railway construction began. White British Columbians knew that the Americans had employed over twelve thousand Chinese workers to build their transcontinental railway during 1863–1869. At the first sitting of British Columbia's new provincial assembly in 1871, one member pressed for two laws. He wanted an annual tax of $50 to be levied on each Chinese in B.C. He wanted to ban any use of Chinese workers on government-funded public works.

White British Columbians disliked the Chinese for several reasons. They said the Chinese worked for lower wages, and took jobs away from white people. They said the Chinese were not settlers and thereby slowed the pace of economic growth. They accused the Chinese of carrying diseases and being a bad moral influence on young people. They said the Chinese could not assimilate into a "Canadian" way of life.

After the railway was finished, Canada made it clear that the Chinese were not wanted here. In the summer of 1885, a law was passed to reduce the number of them entering Canada. From January 1, 1886, onward, every Chinese person coming to Canada had to pay a head tax of $50. As well, the number of Chinese a ship could bring to Canada was limited.

The Canadian Pacific Railway made the idea of a Canada stretching "from sea to shining sea" a reality. Chinese workers were a major part of that accomplishment. In September 1989 a "Memorial to Commemorate the Chinese Railway Workers in Canada" was unveiled in downtown Toronto. The memorial takes the shape of a life-size railway trestle. Part of the memorial's text reads:

> *. . . Far from their families, amid hostile sentiments, these men laboured long hours and made the completion of the railway physically and economically possible. . . . With no means of going back to China when their labour was no longer needed, thousands drifted in near destitution along the completed track. All of them remained nameless in the history of Canada. . . . We erect this monument to remember them.*

Mealtime for Chinese workers aboard a Canadian Pacific Railway Company ship. The date and location of the image are not known, but we can tell that the workers are Chinese because of the Chinese-style jacket worn by the man on the left and by the coiling of queues atop men's heads.

Two Chinese railway workers at a camp near Kamloops, British Columbia. The crews moved from site to site, to be close to construction.

Possibly a rest day for Chinese railway workers. Note the wash basin, belongings being dried, and men gathered in a group.

Workers remove rubble from the path of the railway using wheelbarrows and wooden ramps.

Tunnel #8, about 27 km above Yale, showing the narrow mouth, the river below, and the mountains from which rocks rolled onto the workers. For a sense of scale, note the man standing near the entrance.

C.P.R. locomotive #365 moves acrosss a bridge in the Fraser Canyon.

The section of railway through the Fraser Canyon, with its high cliffs, was one of the most difficult to complete.

NEW
SCHEDULE OF WAGES
FOR
WHITE LABOR
ON THE
CANADIAN
PACIFIC
RAILWAY
IN BRITISH COLUMBIA.

verseers	$125 00 per month.	
Rock Foremen,	$3 00 to $4 00	per day
Earth do	2 25 to 3 00	do
Bridge do	3 00	do
Bridge Carpenters, 1st class,	$3 00	do
do do 2nd class	2 50	do
Masons	$2 50 to 3 50	do
Blacksmiths, 1st class	$3 00	do
do 2nd class	2 50	do
do helpers	1 50 to 2	do
Drillers	$1 75 to 2 00	do
Laborers,	1 50 to 1 75	do
Hewers,	2 50 to 3 00	do
Choppers	1 50 to 2 00	do

All outside labor 10 hours per day.

A. ONDERDONK.
General Manager.

White workers made twice the wage of the Chinese crews.

Glossary

Almanac, Chinese: A guidebook to the days of the year. Among many items, an almanac notes the changes of the seasons, predicts weather and advises if certain days are good for events such as weddings or funerals.

Chek-Hom: A busy market town in Guangdong province in south China.

Ching Ming: This day of observance is held by Chinese families each spring to pay respects to their ancestors at gravesites.

Fan-tan, fan-tan cloth: Fan-tan is a gambling game where money is bet on how many beads are under a cover. The fan-tan cloth is marked with squares where a player may place money to make bets.

Ginger: A plant that is eaten as food, medicine or spice.

Gold Mountain: In the nineteenth century, Chinese immigrants called North America "Gold Mountain" because the gold rushes in California and in British Columbia had drawn them here.

Heavenly Nines: A game played with dominoes.

Horse position: A stance in Chinese martial arts.

Ik-Hoi: A busy market town in Guangdong province in south China.

Incense: Incense is made from aromatic woods, oils and other materials such as spices. When incense is burnt, smoke and fragrant smells are released.

Insects Awaken: A spring day in the Chinese almanac.

Jung-San: A county in Guangdong province, south China.

Lunar calendar: A lunar calendar is based on the cycles of the moon (from new moon to full moon). A lunar cycle repeats every 29.5 days. A solar calendar is based on the earth's revolution around the sun, so one month is one-twelfth of a year, at 30.4 days.

Ming dynasty: A period of imperial rule in China that lasted from 1368 to 1644 CE.

New Year (lunar) customs: Just before the lunar New Year, families in China clean the house thoroughly. People also distribute red packets of gift money to children, feast on special foods and wear new clothes.

Opera, Chinese: Chinese opera tells stories on stage through song, dance and acting. In the nineteenth century, female roles in Chinese opera were played by male actors.

Paddlewheeler: A ship or boat that is propelled by a large wheel containing many paddle blades.

Red Beard Ghosts: In the nineteenth century, Chinese people often called Westerners by this name, which referred to a hair colour that had been rarely seen in Asia. The word "ghost" was used negatively.

Say-Yup: Say-Yup means "Four Counties" and was a region where many Chinese immigrants came from.

Second City: The name Chinese immigrants used for New Westminster, British Columbia.

Toi-San: One of the four counties in Say-Yup, in south China.

Yuan dynasty: A period of imperial rule in China that lasted from 1271 to 1368 CE.

Zhou: A common Chinese surname.

Acknowledgments

Grateful acknowledgment is made for permission to reprint the following:

Cover cameo: *Document with photograph certifying that a certificate of identity was issued, 11/15/1910; Chinese Exclusion Act Case Files, compiled ca. 1882 – ca. 1960,* National Archives and Records Administration, ARC identifier 278696.
Cover scene: *Work Crew Laying Track in the Lower Fraser Valley, 1881,* Royal BC Museum, A-07021.
Cover details: Aged journal © Shutterstock/velora, aged paper © Shutterstock/Filipchuck Oleg Vasilovich, belly band © ranplett/istockphoto, (back cover) label © Shutterstock/Thomas Bethge

Page 223: *Oriental men aboard a Canadian Pacific Railway Company ship. Date, location and photographer unknown,* Vancouver Public Library 12866.
Page 224 (upper): *Chinese Camp, Kamloops, British Columbia, 1886,* Library and Archives Canada, C-021987.
Page 224 (lower): *Construction of a Chinese Camp,* Library and Archives Canada C-016715.
Page 225: *Chinese at work on C.P.R. in mountains,* Ernest Brown/Library and Archives Canada, C-6686.
Page 226: *Tunnel No. 8, 16 ½ Miles Above Yale,* Vancouver Public Library 416.
Page 227: *C.P.R. locomotive #365 on a bridge in the Fraser Canyon,* Vancouver Public Library Accession Number 9556.
Page 228 (right, detail): Schedule of Wages for White Labour on the Canadian Pacific Railway Line, *Inland Sentinel.*
Page 228 (left): Map by Paul Heersink/Paperglyphs. Map data © 1999 Government of Canada with permission from Natural Resources Canada.

The publisher wishes to thank W. Peter Ward and Robert Turner for sharing their historical expertise; and Barbara Hehner for her careful checking of the factual details.

About the Author

Paul Yee tells an intriguing story about growing up Chinese in Canada, but not learning much about the history of Chinese people here. He says, "When I was a child in the 1960s, there were no books about my world — the world of immigrants, racial minorities and different histories. I had to learn about these things much later in life." He heard some stories from his Aunt Lillian, who raised him. She told him a tale about railway-building: "One cold winter day, a worker wandered by mistake into a warehouse. He passed a high shelf. Looking up, he saw round shapes lining the edge. Then he saw that each round shape had a pigtail coiled around it. Those were heads of Chinese workers. The shelf held frozen bodies. The worker ran out as fast as he could."

Paul didn't learn about the Chinese working on the Canadian Pacific Railway until he went to university. "The story wasn't taught anywhere, not even at my Chinese language school," Paul says. "This event had involved thousands of Chinese working at great personal cost to help build one of Canada's defining symbols. Yet their personal stories were not passed down from generation to generation within families. That puzzled me.

"One explanation is this. In the nineteenth century,

south China saw huge numbers of its men go abroad to work, to several countries in southeast Asia, to Australia and to North America. They worked abroad in many fields and sent money home to their families. To them, the Canadian Pacific Railway was just another job. It was tough work, but that was the nature of overseas work.

"Another explanation? Railway construction followed the gold rushes in California and British Columbia. There would have been stories about lucky adventurers who picked up gold in the rivers to take home. Those tales would have dazzled eager listeners. People didn't want to hear about the dirty, back-breaking labour of moving earth and rocks that was part of railway-building.

"I didn't grow up with my parents, so I heard very little family history. In my early twenties, I toured China and my father's village. Word of my visit reached my father's older sister, whom I never knew existed. She wrote to me after I returned to Canada. I wrote back asking her about my grandfather. She said he had worked on the railway. To this day, I wonder if I can believe her 100 per cent."

Paul Yee has written almost twenty picture books and novels, contemporary and historical, about the Chinese experience in Canada. Among his many other honours, he won the Governor General's Award for *Ghost Train*, the B.C. Book Prize for *Tales from Gold Mountain*, a Canada Council Honourable Mention for *The Curses of Third Uncle,* and was nominated for the CLA Book of the Year Award for *Dead Man's Gold and Other Stories.*

Other books in the I AM CANADA Series

Prisoner of Dieppe
World War II
Hugh Brewster

Coming in 2011

Shot at Dawn
World War I
John Wilson

Deadly Voyage
R.M.S. *Titanic*
Hugh Brewster

For more information please see the I AM CANADA website: www.scholastic.ca/iamcanada